KU-655-623

THE NEW COMPLETE GUIDE TO RUNNING
(2ND EDITION)
Editor Wesley Doyle
Art Director Steve Clarke
Production Roger Bilsland

RUNNER'S WORLD UK
Editor Andy Dixon
Contributing Editor Jo Pavey
Group Publishing Director Alun Williams
Sales Director, Hearst Rodale
Luke Robins
Print & Digital Advertising Director
Andrea Sullivan
Brand Manager Katherine Kendall
Head of Marketing and Events Jane Shackleton

HEARST MAGAZINES UK
Chief Executive Officer Anna Jones
Managing Director, Brands Michael Rowley
Chief Financial Officer Claire Blunt
HR Director Surinder Simmons
Business Manager Sarah Hammond
Head of Newstrade Marketing Jennifer Smith
Circulation Manager Bianca Lloyd-Smith

HEARST RODALE JOINT BOARD OF DIRECTORS
**President and CEO, Hearst Magazines
International** Duncan Edwards
**Senior Vice President, International Business
Development and Partnerships,
Rodale International** Robert Novick

RODALE INTERNATIONAL
Rodale Inc, 33 East Minor Street,
Emmaus, Pennsylvania 18098, USA

**Executive Director, Business Development
and Global Licensing** Kevin LaBonge
Director, Global Marketing Tara Swansen
Editorial Director John Ville
**Editorial Director, Runner's World
International** Veronika Taylor
Senior Content Manager Karl Rozemeyer
Production Assistant Denise Weaver
Editorial Assistant Natanya Spies

©2015, Hearst Rodale Ltd
33 Broadwick Street, London, W1F 0DQ
Tel: 020 7339 4400

For annual subscription rates for the UK, please call our enquiry
line on 0844 848 5203. Back issues, customer enquiries, change
of address and orders to: Runner's World, Hearst Magazines
UK Ltd, Tower House, Sovereign Park, Lathkill Street, Market
Harborough, Leics LE16 9EF (0844 848 5203; Mon to Fri,
8am to 9:30pm and Saturday, 8am to 4pm).
Runner's World is published in the United Kingdom by Hearst
Rodale Limited – a joint venture by Hearst Magazines UK,
a wholly owned subsidiary of The Hearst Corporation, and
Rodale International, a division of Rodale Incorporated.

RUNNER'S WORLD IS A TRADEMARK OF, AND IS USED
UNDER LICENCE FROM, RODALE INTERNATIONAL

HEARST MAGAZINES UK ENVIRONMENTAL POLICY
All paper used to make this book is from sustainable
sources and we encourage our suppliers to join an accredited
green scheme. Magazines are fully recyclable.
Go to recyclenow.com to find your nearest sites.

WELCOME

The UK is a running nation. Last year there were nearly 200 organised marathons, membership of over 1,200 registered running clubs has never been higher and every Saturday morning an average of 70,000 people line up in 376 locations to run a 5K in the name of fun. We've got the running bug and we've got it bad.

Everywhere you look on streets and in parks there are brightly clad runners of every shape, size and ability doing their stuff. Of course, it's one of the easiest sports to take up: it's just left foot, right foot, repeat. But if you want to improve or have a specific goal in mind, it's worth getting some sound advice – and that's where this book comes in. It's a compilation of the best tips, hardest-won wisdom and cutting-edge scientific opinion from the network of experts on the world's biggest-selling running magazine.

There are common-sense training plans (from 5K to marathon); fad-free weight-loss tips; and sage advice on how to improve your form, buy the right kit, fuel your body, avoid injury and much more.

Beginner or club vet, speed demon or back-of-the-packer, keen bean or weekend warrior – there's something in here for you. Say hello to the runner you're about to be.

RUNNER'S WORLD

THE NEW COMPLETE GUIDE TO *RUNNING*

16 REASONS TO RUN

32

TOP TRAINING TIPS

165
GET THE RUNNER'S HIGH

 CHAPTER **4**

HEALTH & INJURY

 DON'T GET HURT
Suffer from constant niggles and pains? Here's a handy guide telling you what to do (and what not to do) to keep yourself free from pain and injury.

THE RUNNER'S MOT
Everyone needs a once-over now and again. So make sure you're fit for purpose and give yourself an MOT with these four easy-to-do self-checks.

THE SCIENCE OF RECOVERY
What you do when you're not running is just as important as what you do when you are. We asked experts to explain the benefits of various methods of recovery.

 SOFT LANDING
Ditch the road work and move onto a more forgiving surface to cut down on joint pain and injury risk.

 PILLOW TALK
Have a lie-in and improve your performance while you sleep.

 INJURY CLINIC
The top five runners' ailments: how you can identify them and what you can do about them.

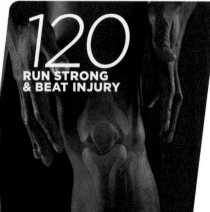

120
RUN STRONG & BEAT INJURY

 CHAPTER **5**

MOTIVATION

48 WAYS TO KEEP GOING
Mental tips and tricks to ensure you start well and finish strong.

 **BEAT THE CLOCKS**
Can't fit a run into your busy schedule? Here's how to always find the time.

 QUICK THINKING
Your grey matter can get you a PB. We show you how to train your mind as well as your muscles.

ONE-TRACK MIND
Get your brain and body in sync and working together.

WINNING THE MIND GAME
Easy-to-remember mental mantras to improve your running performance.

184
TIPS FOR WOMEN

LOOKING AHEAD
Your new running
journey starts here

CHAPTER | **1**

GETTING
STARTED

Your guide to becoming a better runner – whether you're new to the sport or just want to know more

GET OUTSIDE
There's nothing better than a run

49 REASONS TO LOVE *RUNNING*

Apart from improved fitness and better health what has running ever given us? Well, quite a lot actually...

1 SAY GOODBYE TO YOUR BELLY

University of Dublin research found a 10-stone adult burns 391 calories in 30 minutes of running, compared with 277 calories while cycling, and 272 calories while playing tennis. Translation? You blitz your belly up to 40 per cent faster.

2 BULLET-PROOF YOUR BONES

Fifteen minutes of light jogging just three times a week is all it can take to reduce your risk of developing osteoporosis in later life by up to 40 per cent, according to research from the National Osteoporosis Society.

3 BLITZ BODY BLEMISHES

'Running tones the buttocks and thighs quicker than any other exercise, which literally squeezes out the lingering fat,' according to Dr James Fleming, author of *Beat Cellulite Forever* (Piatkus).

4 LAUGH AT THE WEATHER

It doesn't matter if the weather forecast shows rain, cold, wind – there's no excuse not to get out. Just layer up depending on how the skies look and see it as another challenge. It's an activity that is made bespoke for the rather unpredictable weather we have in this country.

5 GET H-A-P-P-Y

'Mild to moderate exercise releases natural, feel-good endorphins that help counter stress,' explains Andrew McCulloch, chief executive of the Mental Health Foundation. So if you're feeling down and want cheering up break out your trainers and hit the road.

6 HAVE THE WORLD TO YOURSELF

Very few things are worth getting out of bed for, but an early-morning run is definitely one of them. There's a certain satisfaction – some might say smugness – in the knowledge that while the rest of the world is yawning, you're out exercising and enjoying the magic of the sunrise. Running on deserted city streets or quiet country lanes is a great way to start the day for both your mind and your body.

7 IMPROVE YOUR QUALITY OF SLEEP

Stanford University School of Medicine researchers asked sedentary insomnia sufferers to jog for 20-30 minutes on alternate days. The result? The time it took them to fall asleep was reduced by half, while the time they spent actually asleep increased by almost an hour.

8 WIN YOURSELF SOME MEDALS

Silverware isn't just for Olympians. All you need to do is enter a race, make sure you get to the end of it, and you'll be given a nice medal to stick on your mantelpiece – perhaps the first of many – to prove what you've achieved.

9 GET REGULAR

According to experts from Bristol University, the benefits of running go from your head all the way down to your... bottom. 'Physical activity helps decrease the time for food to move through the large intestine, limiting the amount of water absorbed back into your body, leaving you with softer stools that are easier to pass,' explains gastroenterologist Dr Ken Heaton.

10 KEEP THE DOCTOR AT BAY

'Moderate exercise makes immune cells more active, so they're ready to fight off infection,' says Cath Collins, chief dietitian at St George's Hospital in London. In studies conducted at the University of North Carolina, US, candidates who jogged for just 15 minutes five days a week took half as many sick days as those couch potatoes who never get their running shoes out of the wardrobe, let alone lace them up.

11 SEE THE WORLD

What other sport offers you the chance to travel to all four corners of the earth in the name of fitness? From the New York to Rio de Janeiro marathons, to seeing parts of our own sceptred isle you never even knew existed, it's a veritable ticket to ride.

12 GUILT-FREE SNACKING

Upping your salt intake is advice you seldom hear from your doctor, but in the last few days before a marathon that's exactly what you should do – giving you the perfect excuse to munch on crisps. The salt in them helps protect against hyponatraemia, a condition caused by drinking too much water without enough sodium, which can lead to illness and, in rare cases, death.

13 YOU DON'T NEED INSTRUCTIONS

If you can walk, you can run. Think back to your days of being a child and you will realise that running around or on track is actually one of our most natural instincts.

14 PROTECT YOUR TICKER

Maintaining a healthy heart is vital for everyone and running is a great way to achieve this. Studies from Purdue University, US, have shown that regular running can cut your risk of heart disease by 50 per cent.

15 GET TIME BACK ON YOUR SIDE

Whether loosely lodged in your mental to-do list or typed into your iPhone, your daily workout should be an important entry in your day-to-day schedule. It helps you organise everything else you need to do, often into B.R. (Before Run) and A.R. (After Run) time frames, as well as giving you much-needed time to yourself to be able to absorb and ponder the rest of your daily itinerary.

16 REACH CREATIVE BREAKTHROUGHS

Writers, musicians, artists and other creative professionals use running to help solve mental blocks and aid must-do-it-today decision making. For this we can credit the increased flow of oxygen to the grey matter when it is needed most, sparking the brain's neurons and giving them – and you – time and breathing space away from 'real life.'

WORLD TOUR
Turn globe trotting into globe running

17 THINK FASTER

Researchers from Illinois University, US, found that a five per cent improvement in cardio-respiratory fitness led to an improvement of up to 15 per cent in mental tests.

18 YOU CAN BE AN ALL-ROUNDER

Whether you want to keep in shape like former F1 champion Jenson Button, or go 12 hard rounds like boxer Amir Khan, running is the place to begin.

19 CLIMBS CULL CALORIES

Find a decent incline, take a deep breath (at the bottom, not the top) and incorporate it into your programme to burn up to 40 per cent more calories – the average 11st runner will burn 1,299 calories

a lot together – it's the start of a beautiful relationship.

24 MAKE A DIFFERENCE

Millions of runners worldwide turn their determination to get fitter and healthier into fund-raising efforts for the less fortunate. For example, the Virgin Money London Marathon is the largest annual fundraising event in the world, having brought over £716 million into the coffers of good causes. Running for charity will give you a warm glow inside as well as out.

25 THE JOY OF FINDING A NEW ROUTE

Today you took a left rather than a right and suddenly found amazing views and a piece of solitude you never knew existed. Imagine how many more runs there are out there just waiting for you to discover them.

26 INDULGE YOUR WANDERLUST

Forgets a cab, there's simply no better way of getting to know a new city than hitting the streets on foot. And if you run you'll become familiar with the area much quicker. As well as giving you the necessary orientation, it'll energise you after your journey, reset your biological clock to a new time zone and give you the chance to meet locals face-to-face. Much better – and cheaper – than seeing the sights from the back seat of a taxi.

running a 10 per cent incline for an hour, compared with 922 on the flat. The only way is up.

20 BOOST YOUR SEX LIFE

A study from Cornell University in the US found male runners have the sexual prowess of men two to five years younger, while females can delay the menopause by a similar amount of time. Meanwhile, research carried out at Harvard University found men over 50 who run at least three hours a week have a 30 per cent lower risk of impotence than those who do little or no exercise.

21 IT CAN REPLACE DEPENDENCIES...

...such as smoking, alcoholism, or overeating with positive alternatives, says William

Glasser, author of *Positive Addiction* (HarperPerennial Books). So if you're trying to quit something, add running to your routine. You'll find yourself a happier and healthier person by getting the kind of fix that adds to, rather than detracts from, the good things in life.

22 END BOREDOM

Even the most mundane errand can be transformed into a training run; from posting a letter to taking the dog for some much-needed exercise, suddenly every journey has a double purpose.

23 THAT NEW-SHOE SMELL

You've tried on and sampled your top picks and made your choice. Now they're here, in your hands. You'll go through

27 THE KNOWING RACE-START NOD

You're at the start line and the race is about to begin. You see a face you recognise from the last meet. Out of mutual respect and an acknowledgement of the challenge to come, you look at each other and nod. Nobody else knows it, but the gauntlet has been thrown down and the race is now on. ▰

28 GET A NATURAL HIGH

Comparing the pre- and post-run scans of runners, neurologists from the University of Bonn, Germany, found greater evidence of the happy hormone endorphin in the frontal and limbic regions of the brain after running. These areas are involved in processing emotions and stress, which means you may experience what's known as the 'runner's high'.

29 YOU'VE GOT A FRIEND FOR LIFE

We all go through phases in our lives, including times when we run less. You may get a job that demands more of your time. You may have to spend more time having and caring for a new baby. Maybe you simply go on holiday or take a sabbatical. That's fine. Running adapts itself easily to your ebbs and flows. Best of all, running is always there to take the strain when you need it most.

30 JOIN A CLUB, LIVE FOR LONGER

A nine-year study from Harvard Medical School found that surrounding yourself with friends who also run reduces blood pressure and strengthens the immune system. This can result in a 60 per cent reduction in your overall risk of death. Joining a running club is the best way to find yourself some new life-lenthening acquaintances.

31 THE NUMBERS DO NOT LIE

There's no place for dishonesty when it comes to running, from distances you cover to times on the stopwatch. It's really very simple: you get back what you put in.

32 SPEND QUALITY TIME AS A FAMILY

It's one of the few activities that the whole family can do together. The smallest tyke can clamber into their jogging buggy, fit parents and grandparents can take turns pushing, and Junior can follow along on his new two-wheeler. Hundreds of races include events for all the family.

33 EXCUSE FOR A MASSAGE

Post-race, indulge in a professional massage and enjoy the relaxed feeling as you float back to real life.

34 BURN MORE FAT

Your calorie burn doesn't stop when you do. 'As little as 20-30 minutes will burn a higher amount of total calories for hours after,' says sports physiologist Mark Simpson from Loughborough University's School of Sports Science.

35 BOOST YOUR BELLOWS

When running, an adult uses about 10 times the oxygen they would need when sitting in front of the television for the same period. Over time, regular jogging will strengthen the cardiovascular system, enabling your heart and lungs to work more efficiently, getting more oxygen where it's needed, quicker. This means you can do more exercise for less effort. How good does that sound?

36 APPRECIATE THE ENVIRONMENT

We all now know that Global Warming isn't a myth and we all have our part to play in ensuring the survival of our planet for generations to come. You crave fresh, clean air when you run. You long for soft trails, towering trees, pure water. You have plenty of time to ponder the big questions. You resolve: save the earth.

37 THAT SPECIAL 'PB' FEELING

Remember that the 'P' here stands for 'personal' – you set the goals, you put the work in, you get the results. Savour it.

38 OUTRUN THE REAPER

Kings College London researchers compared more than 2,400 identical twins, and found that those who did the equivalent of just three 30-minute jogs a week were nine years 'biologically younger', even after discounting other influences, including body mass index (BMI) and smoking.

39 BUILDS DISCIPLINE

Practice makes perfect, in running and in life. The most successful people are those with a modest amount of talent and a huge amount of discipline. Running will give you the discipline – the talent is down to you.

40 IT'S NOT ELITIST

You're struggling in last place but get the biggest cheer. You deserve it; after all, you've been running for longer than anyone else. There aren't many other sports where last place receives as much applause as the winners.

RIGHT ON TARGET
Getting out on the road
really hits the spot

41 SIZE REALLY DOESN'T MATTER

Running can be a great activity and good way to stay in shape for everybody type. No matter when you choose to start, there are no barriers to just getting out there and giving it a go.

42 YOU'RE THE ONE IN CONTROL

Whatever the pressures of your daily life, be it your work or personal life, you have the final say in how much or little running you choose to do.

43 HELPS MOTHER AND BABY

Pregnant women who regularly exercise during their pregnancy can have an easier, less complicated labour, a quicker recovery and better overall mood throughout the nine months, according to researchers at Michigan University in the US. For a good example look no further than mother and marathon record holder Paula Radcliffe.

44 HIT THE MARK

Some runners set distance or time goals, many will instead focus on improving their health or losing weight; others run simply to unwind, relax or have a place to think freely. Running can help you in achieving any goal that you choose to set your mind to.

45 RUN AND STAY YOUNG

'Exercise creates the ideal environment within the body to optimise collagen production, which supports the skin, helping to reduce the appearance of fine lines and wrinkles,' explains Dr Christopher Rowland Payne (thelondonclinic.co.uk).

46 AGE IS NO BARRIER

Just ask 77-year-old legend Ron Hill, who hasn't missed a single day's running since December 1964.

47 EVERY RUN IS A JOURNEY

You never know what you might find or who or what you might see. Even more interesting, who knows what thoughts might flash into your mind? Today's run could truly change your life in a way that you could never have imagined when you pulled on your kit, put on your shoes and headed out of the door.

48 YOUR PERSONAL THERAPIST

There's no greater escape from the pressures and stresses of modern life than slipping on your trainers and getting out there. It's just you and the road – giving you time to organise your life, think things through and invariably finish in a better place than when you set off.

49 IT'S FREE

Going for a run doesn't cost a penny. There's no need to join a club straight away and all you need are a decent pair of running shoes, shorts and a top to get started. The world is your running track, go out and enjoy it. ■

HOW RUNNING CHANGED **MY LIFE**

RW readers share their stories of how our sport helped turn their lives around. If you're searching for inspiration to get out and run, look no further...

■ I couldn't run for more than 30 seconds when I started but after 18 months I'd lost 5st and now I'm running 10-milers and planning to do my first half marathon.
MICHAEL NUTTALL

■ Running helped me beat my weight issues – I was 21st but I'm now 13st, have a 10K PB of 44 minutes and have run a marathon.
RICHARD HODGKINS

■ Having had self-confidence issues, running has helped me feel better about myself. It has become my therapy.
CARRIE CHALLONER

■ Running gave me back myself.
CHRISTINA NEWNHAM

■ It's a commitment that pulls you away from the negativity of life and leads you on a journey of happiness and wonder.
KATY VATTEROTT

■ Running saved my life. I lost 10st 8lb in a year and I'm now heading for the 53-mile Highland Fling. Totally hooked!
RUTH HOWIE

■ Running was the only thing that kept the panic at bay during a bout of depression five years ago. I ran a 3:30 marathon that year, too.
SEAN ROE

■ I was getting divorced when friends convinced me to join a running club. It's a great feeling that we all have this thing in common.
JON-PAUL KEARNS

■ Running keeps me close to my Dad – he loved the sport.
KAREN ELSTOB

■ Running has saved me from some very low moments and helped me regain my confidence after an abusive relationship. I really couldn't do without it.
JO ALLCOCK

■ Running helps me live with my bipolar daily. It's a lifesaver for me.
JULIE HODGSON

■ It's helped me put my life in perspective. When I'm stressed, all I have to do is run and the world is a better place.
DAWN FAILES

■ Running keeps my happy levels topped up.
CHARLOTTE CAHILL

■ Running saved me from annihilation after my husband died in 2011. I found peace and a new life through it.
SUZANNE HOLLAND

■ Running has given me the confidence to achieve things I never thought I could.
HELEN BAXTER

■ A year and a half ago I was diagnosed with severe sleep apnea. Now, after losing two stone through running, I'm cured.
NICHOLAS SMITH

■ I got into running after battling against alcoholism. I am eight years sober and enjoy my running so much I rarely crave alcohol at all.
JOSH WOODSTOCK

■ After a stroke I could only walk for a few minutes. A year later I ran a 10K. Running gave me a new sense of life.
SAMANTHA COLLIER

■ Running is the best drug in the world – it gives me a buzz plus a sense of achievement. It's changed my life.
DAVID TILLETT

■ Running has saved me from a life of chronic back pain.
SALLY MCCABE

■ I was depressed to the point of a breakdown. Running snapped me out of it. I lost weight and made new friends.
STEVE CLARINGBOLD

■ I started running late and its impact on my clinical depression keeps me going. I'll never be fast but once I'm out there, my pace soon pales into insignificance.
MAXINE GRIMSHAW

■ When I stopped smoking I wanted to replace it with something healthy. Running has changed me, inside and out. I can't imagine life without it.
CLAIRE JONES

■ I feel blessed to still be running in my 55th year. I've loved it since I was 14 and still do. Sadly, I suffered a stroke five years ago, but running kept me going. I'm so glad to have run with Croydon Harriers in the early days and Widnes Wasps now.
DEANSIE PHILLIPS

■ Running saved me from heartbreak. Rather than feeling sorry for myself I decided to focus on running a marathon. And it worked – my life has changed so much for the better.
CATHY AYTON

UP AND AT THEM
Fitness is only a few
steps from the sofa

STARTERS
ORDERS

Ready to begin your life as a runner? Our experts are here to answer your questions to give you the knowledge you need to get off on the right foot

A journey of a thousand miles begins with a single step, wrote Chinese philosopher Lao Tzu. He was right, metaphorically as well as literally, and rarely do his words ring more true – in both senses – than when you're learning to run. The journey may be long and it may be challenging; and there won't be an instant fix, a 10-minute miracle or an effort-free shortcut. But if you stick with it, you'll get to where you want to be – whether that's healthier, slimmer, the proud owner of a race medal, or any combination of goals.

Whatever your initial motivation for lacing up those running shoes, it won't be long before you can stop calling yourself a 'beginner'. Before you know it you'll be a fully fledged runner – having fun, getting fit and able to turn with confidence to whatever goals you choose next. We'll help you get there. To succeed you must follow a sensible training plan, which you'll find here, along with a starter pack of know-how to get you going and keep you motivated.

All you need is a strong mind and the will to put your body in motion. Your legs will carry you, but only after your brain tells them to. And only you can commit to a beginner's running plan, lace up, get going and not stop until you achieve what you want. Start today. You'll never find a better time than right now. ▶

Illustrations **Andrew Lyons**

ABOUT THE EXPERTS

Bart Yasso The legendary coach has worked with runners of all abilities over the last 30 years.

Paul Hobrough The former GB athlete is a physiotherapist who specialises in running. (physioandtherapy.co.uk).

Amby Burfoot The *Runner's World* US Editor at Large and winner of the 1968 Boston Marathon has been writing about running since the 1970s.

Jennifer Van Allen A running coach who specialises in designing programmes for, and working with, beginner runners.

WHY *RUN?*

Well, it will make you fitter, healthier, happier and smarter

RUNNER'S HIGH
Every run can be a
journey of discovery

evidence that it helps prevent it. A recent review of 170 studies, in the *Journal of Nutrition,* showed that regular exercise is associated with a lower risk of developing certain cancers, including colon cancer (risk reduced by 40-70 per cent), breast cancer (30-40 per cent) and lung cancer (30-40 per cent).

4 FEEL HAPPIER EVERY DAY
Research has shown that half an hour of running, five days a week for just three weeks boosts sleep quality, mood and concentration during the day. Other studies have shown that exercise helps you cope with anxiety and stress even after you've finished your session.

5 KEEP YOUR MIND YOUNG AND SHARP
Running regularly will counteract the ageing of your grey matter and help you stay sharp. Recent research published in *Psychonomic Bulletin & Review* concluded that the evidence is 'insurmountable' that regular exercise helps curb age-related mental decline.

6 PROTECT YOUR KNEES AND BONES
Once you start running, it's a certainty you'll have family, friends and even strangers telling you that 'running is bad for your knees'. However, the scientific evidence has proven that it's not. In fact, studies have shown that it improves knee health. Plus, running increases bone mass and helps stem age-related bone loss.

1 BURN EXTRA CALORIES... ON THE SOFA
You already know that running burns calories. What you may not know is that the effect continues even after you stop. Studies have shown that regular exercise boosts 'afterburn' – a term that refers to the number of calories you burn post-exercise. Even better news is you don't have to be sprinting, either, as the afterburn is triggered when you run just slightly faster than your easy, conversational pace.

2 LIVE A MUCH LONGER LIFE
Just 30 minutes of exercise a day, five days a week, is enough to add years to your life. Various studies have shown the life-extending benefits of exercise, even in people who may feel wary of starting, such as those already suffering from conditions like heart disease.

3 PROTECT YOURSELF FROM CANCER
Running doesn't cure cancer, but there's plenty of

ARE YOU A NEW RUNNER?

NO → Why are you here? You know all this stuff already.

YES

YOU NEED:
THE RIGHT RUNNING SHOES
Get yourself fitted at a specialist running shop. Wearing the wrong shoes may contribute to injury, says running-specialist physio Tom Labisch.

YES **LIAR!**

DO YOU ENJOY HAVING BLISTERS?

NO

YOU NEED:
SPECIALIST, SWEAT-WICKING RUNNING SOCKS
Spending a lot on shoes and then skimping on socks is a mistake. Cotton socks are less comfortable and greatly increase your blister risk.

YOU NEED:
A GPS WATCH
These use satellites to record your distance (and display data). Smartphone apps such as Strava and RunKeeper will also do this, but phones are heavier and harder to look at on the run.

AND

YOU NEED:
SWEAT-WICKING KIT
Cotton absorbs sweat, leaving clothing sopping and heavy. Kit that's made from moisture-wicking material transports sweat away from your skin, leaving you to run in comfort.

TREADMILL

ARE YOU RUNNING ON A TREADMILL OR OUTSIDE?

OUTSIDE

WOULD IT PAIN YOU TO RUN 2.96 MILES WHEN YOU MEANT TO RUN 3.1?

NO

UGH. YES.

YOU NEED:
A FOAM ROLLER
If you don't have a personal sports masseuse on staff, a foam roller is one of the best DIY methods to stave off overuse injuries. They come with instructions, too. Be warned, using one can smart a bit.

My legs are sore and tender.

WHAT HURTS AFTER YOU RUN?

NO

IS IT WARM? AND/OR DO YOU GET THIRSTY ON THE RUN?

YES

YOU NEED:
A RUNNING JACKET FOR WINTER
Look for weatherproofing plus breathability, a slim ergonomic fit and stretch in the fabric, so it moves well as you run.

NOTHING.

LUCKY!

My inner thighs and/or arms and/or nipples get rubbed raw.

YOU NEED:
A WATER BOTTLE
Find one that's shaped to fit comfortably in your hand. Or if you'd rather go hands-free, try a hydration pack.

HOW LONG ARE YOU RUNNING FOR?

More than an hour.

Less than an hour.

YOU NEED:
EXTRA FUEL
If you'll be running for over an hour, your body will need a mid-run source of energy that's easy to digest, says Nancy Clark, author of Food Guide for New Runners (£12.95, Meyer & Meyer Sport).

YOU NEED:
LUBE
Apply the lube pre-run to chafing-prone spots to prevent friction. These sports-specific products don't come with embarrassment on purchase – they often look like sticks of deodorant.

YES

YOU NEED:
COMPRESSION SOCKS
Graduated pressure enhances blood flow, bringing extra oxygen and speeding the process of removing post-exercise waste products.

CONGRATS! YOU HAVE EVERYTHING YOU NEED

NO

ARE YOU DOING SPEEDWORK AND/OR TEMPO RUNS?

YES

DO YOU WANT TO LOOK LIKE A PRO AND/OR HELP YOUR MUSCLES RECOVER FASTER POST-RUN?

NO

DO YOU REALLY NEED *THAT?*

Stepping into a specialist running shop can be daunting. Use this chart to work out which pieces of gear, kit and tech you need

STUFF YOU NEED TO *KNOW*

When you start running, you'll have questions.
And our experts have the answers

faster runners to come through. If you're running on a treadmill, make sure you go slow enough to run normally – gripping the handrails can lead to injury.

Q WHEN SHOULD I RUN?
Quite simply, plan to run whenever you're most likely to get it done. Many runners find it's generally easier to fit in a session first thing in the morning. However, if that doesn't suit your daily schedule, find a regular time that does. Then – and this is the most important thing – reserve this slot for running. Don't forget your gear, don't get distracted and don't look for excuses (they can be very easy to find).

Q WHERE SHOULD I RUN?
Find safe, traffic-free routes that you can regularly use in all kinds of weather conditions. If you're running on the road and there's no footpath, run against the traffic, unless you're approaching a blind bend, in which case you should swap sides until it's safe to cross back. When you're ready to venture onto a running track, always run anticlockwise and stay clear of the inner lanes to allow

Q HOW SHOULD I START OFF EACH RUN?
Go into every run with the idea fixed in your mind that you're going to finish strong. No matter how long you plan to run, start out slowly to warm up, then gradually raise your heart rate as you go.

Q HOW FAST SHOULD I RUN?
If you have so much spare lung capacity that you could sing while you run, you're probably going too

slow. If you are huffing and puffing, you're going too fast. A good rule of thumb is that you should be able to hold a conversation. Adjust your pace to stay at the right effort level.

Q HOW DO I TACKLE HILLS?
Hills are a killer, whatever level you're at, so don't feel bad about slowing down on them. The key to conquering hills is to focus on maintaining an even effort – not speed – when ascending and descending. If you find you're gasping for air, slow down or take a walk break.

Q BUT AREN'T WALK BREAKS CHEATING?

Not at all; they're a good idea for many new runners. They stave off muscle fatigue and delay depletion of your glycogen stores – your prime source of energy. This allows you to run for a longer total time than if you ran continuously. You don't have to take them if you don't need them, and you'll naturally reduce them as you improve.

Q HOW DO I KNOW HOW FAR TO RUN?

Don't worry about the number of miles when you're just starting out. Better to focus on building overall fitness and making exercise a habit. Plus, the health benefits result from the time you consistently spend elevating your heart rate. So, to start with, just get out there. When you're more experienced and confident consider investing in some gadgetry to record your data (see *Do You Really Need That?*, previous page).

Q SHOULD I TRY TO RUN EVERY DAY?

Not straight away. It's important to give your body time to recover so it can adapt to the training schedule and the new demands being made on it. Aim for three to five days a week.

Q WHAT DO I DO IF I GET TIRED?

When the effort feels tough, it's very common for runners to tense up. If this happens, it helps to unknit your brow, unclench your jaw and keep your hands relaxed. If you're still struggling, slow down. You need to worry about taking on fuel only when your runs start extending beyond the hour mark.

Q WHAT DO I DO IF I MISS A RUN?

Pick up where you left off and don't feel bad. Even if you've missed several runs, you haven't lost as much fitness as you think you have.

The important thing is not to let it derail you. Think of running as a long-term project and put the missed run(s) in the context of the hundreds you'll do over the coming years. There's plenty of time.

Q WHAT DO I DO ABOUT SORENESS?

Pain all over, which eases the more you move is probably delayed onset muscle soreness (DOMS), which is normal as your body adapts. Pain centred on one area, such as the knee, and hurts more when you move, could be a sign of injury and you should visit a physio.

Q WHEN SHOULD I STRETCH?

Pre-run range-of-movement stretches – such as high knees, heel flicks and side-stepping – are good for preparing your body for a run. After, static stretches, held for 45-60 seconds, will restore muscle length, aid recovery and reduce injury risk. ∎

HERE'S YOUR PLAN

This plan, developed by Amby Burfoot, will help you make the transition from walking to running – without walk breaks – in just eight weeks. Don't worry about how fast – or slow – you run, it's simply about putting in the time on your feet.

WEEK	MON	TUES	WED	THURS	FRI	SAT	SUN
1	Run 1 min; walk 2 min; repeat 10x	Walk easy 30 min	Run 1 min; walk 2 min; repeat 10x	Walk easy 30 min	Run 1 min; walk 2 min; repeat 10x	Run 1 min; walk 2 min; repeat 10x	Rest
2	Run 2 min; walk 1 min; repeat 10x	Walk easy 30 min	Run 3 min; walk 1 min; repeat 7x; run 2 min	Walk easy 30 min	Run 4 min; walk 1 min; repeat 6x	Run 4 min; walk 1 min; repeat 6x	Rest
3	Run 5 min; walk 1 min; repeat 5x	Walk easy 30 min	Run 5 min; walk 1 min; repeat 5x	Walk easy 30 min	Run 6 min; walk 1 min; repeat 4x; run 2 min	Run 6 min; walk 1 min; repeat 4x; run 2 min	Rest
4	Run 8 min; walk 1 min; repeat 3x; run 3 min	Walk easy 30 min	Run 9 min; walk 1 min; repeat 3x	Walk easy 30 min	Run 10 min; walk 1 min; repeat 2x; run 8 min	Run 11 min; walk 1 min; repeat 2x; run 6 min	Rest
5	Run 12 min; walk 1 min; repeat 2x; run 4 min	Walk easy 30 min	Run 13 min; walk 1 min; repeat 2x; run 2 min	Walk easy 30 min	Run 14 min; walk 1 min; repeat 2x	Run 15 min; walk 1 min; run 14 min	Rest
6	Run 16 min; walk 1 min; run 13 min	Walk easy 30 min	Run 17 min; walk 1 min; run 12 min	Walk easy 30 min	Run 18 min; walk 1 min; run 11 min	Run 19 min; walk 1 min; run 10 min	Rest
7	Run 20 min; walk 1 min; run 9 min	Walk easy 30 min	Run 22 min; walk 1 min; run 7 min	Walk easy 30 min	Run 24 min; walk 1 min; run 5 min	Run 26 min; walk 1 min; run 3 min	Rest
8	Run 27 min; walk 1 min; run 2 min	Walk easy 30 min	Run 28 min; walk 1 min; run 1 min	Walk easy 30 min	Run 29 min; walk 1 min	Run 30 min	Rest

BEST IN *SHOE*

There's no 'one shoe suits all' with running.
Here's how to find the right type for you

R unning shoes can be divided into four main categories – neutral cushioned, stability, lightweight and trail – which, for all the bright colours and crazily named high-tech features, are basically designed to suit different people's biomechanical needs.

The full breakdown opposite will give you a greater understanding of what the four different types offer, and should start to give you some idea of what kind of shoe will suit you best. But you shouldn't buy your first pair before visiting a biomechanics expert or, more realistically, an experienced specialist running shop to get a 'gait analysis' done. They look at how your foot strikes the ground to help you choose a shoe with the right level of support.

BEST FOOT FIRST

It should be relatively easy for most runners to find their ideal shoe armed with the right advice. Once you've determined which category you fall into, you have a wide range of shoes to choose from. All you have to do is decide which shoe within your category provides the best comfort, fit and performance for your needs – although that can be a daunting prospect for a beginner. Try out a range of shoes, listen to the advice and don't rush into a decision if you're unsure. ∎

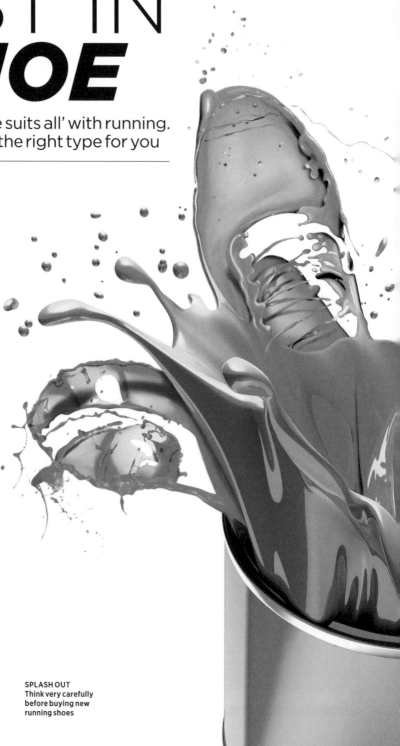

SPLASH OUT
Think very carefully
before buying new
running shoes

WHAT DO I **NEED?**

Before consulting an expert, use our guide to the different trainer types to ensure you're not blinded by science and get the shoe that best suits you

STABILITY
Recommended for those who are mild to moderate overpronators (their feet roll excessively inwards as they strike the ground) and have low to normal arches. These runners tend to need a shoe that has a combination of good support and midsole cushioning.

NEUTRAL CUSHIONED
This type of trainer is best suited to runners who need maximum midsole cushioning and minimum arch support. They suit biomechanically efficient runners and midfoot or forefoot strikers who have high or normal arches.

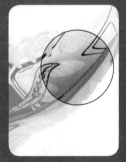

LIGHTWEIGHT
Lighter than average these shoes also vary greatly. Performance shoes are for racing, while minimal shoes offer a little cushioning but still allow your foot to move naturally. 'Barefoot' shoes are lightest, offering little or no cushioning.

TRAIL
Designed for running off road, trail shoes are generally more ruggedly built than road shoes. They offer cushioning with a deeper tread for more grip on variable surfaces, and features such as reinforced toes to protect your feet.

Photography **Studio 33, Getty**

YOUR FIT
KIT

You don't need much gear to run, so it's worth thinking carefully about what you do buy. Here's what to look for

LEGGINGS

T-SHIRTS

SHORTS

FEATURES YOU WANT...

+ **An elasticated waistband for added comfort**
+ Fluorescent piping for safer running at night
+ **Small pocket for holding change, keys, etc**
+ Panelling, which creates a comfortable ergonomic fit

FEATURES YOU WANT...

+ **Flatlock seams add comfort by reducing chafing**
+ Wicking material will transfer sweat away from your body
+ **A UV protective coating for running in the sun**
+ Anti-odour technology for whiff-free training

FEATURES YOU WANT...

+ **An elasticated waistband that won't dig in**
+ Reflective strips to make night running safer
+ **Small pocket for keeping money and keys safe**
+ Webbing inside to hold everything in place

Photography **Studio 33**

JACKETS

FEATURES YOU WANT...

+ **Adjustable waistband and cuffs for added comfort**
+ Strong weather-resistant material for durability
+ **Soft, non-rubbing fabric to avoid chafing**
+ An ergonomic design to allow ease of movement

SOCKS

FEATURES YOU WANT...

+ **Elasticated arch lock to support your feet**
+ Padded soles provide comfort and help prevent blisters
+ **Seam-free toe section to avoid rubbing and nail snags**
+ Breathable, anti-chafe material will keep your feet cool and fresh

RUN IN COMFORT
It pays to be brand agnostic when choosing kit

GARMIN

Distance
26.2
Timer
3:58:33
Lap Pace
9:28

TRAINING WATCHES

If you want to achieve a certain goal, or simply keep a log of your progress as a runner, information is king. Investing in a sports watch need not break the bank and today there are watches to suit everyone, regardless of your budget or level of affinity with technology. Watches can range from £80 to £400 depending on the level of sophistication. Here are the key features you should expect to find in each price range.

BUDGET (£80-£150)

CLEAR VISIBILITY You should be able to clearly read the figures on the watch face while on the run.

CHRONOGRAPH You should at least be able to time the total length of your run and keep tabs on individual lap times if you're interval training.

DATA LOG You don't always have time to review your data after training so your device should be able to store the information from a number of training sessions.

EASY FUNCTIONALITY Using your watch should not require a session consulting the manual before you set out on the run. It should be relatively easy and intuitive to operate.

MID-RANGE (£150-£250)

HEART RATE MONITOR Training to a specific heart rate is a useful alternative to running within target speed zones. A decent mid-range watch should be able to monitor your beats per minute and calculate averages.

SPEED AND DISTANCE How fast, how far, how long: these are the basic information requirements of someone training to hit a target time for a race. Your watch will either measure these things using a pedometer strapped to your foot or, if more high-spec, using GPS technology built into the watch itself.

CALORIE COUNTER If you are running to watch your weight, this is essential.

HIGH-END (£250-£400)

ALTITUDE COUNTER A top-of-the-range watch will measure how many metres you climb – useful if you're training for a particularly hilly race.

TRAINING ZONES It's useful to be able to set parameters for your run, whether speed, heart rate, pace or another gauge. On the best watches you can set alarms to go off if you stray outside of your target zone.

DATA UPLOAD Top-end devices can upload your training stats (either through USB connection or wirelessly) to an online training log where you can analyse your performance in more detail. Often they'll allow you to share the information with friends through social media.

SPORTS BRAS

A good sports bra is as essential a piece of kit for female runners as the right shoes. But which one should you go for?

A BUYER'S GUIDE

'To ensure the right fit try several brands, styles and sizes,' advises Amanda Brasher, senior buyer for specialist running retailer Sweatshop. 'Many women rush into buying a size or style only to find that it's unsuitable so don't be afraid to experiment to find your perfect fit.' Here are Brasher's top tips:

THE UNDERBAND should be tight without digging in with no more than two-and-a-half centimetres' give.

CUPS should encase each breast fully with no wrinkling or gaping, or flesh bulging.

STRAPS should have only two to two-and-a-half centimetres' give. They should be adjustable to fit each individual breast (most busts are slightly asymmetrical).

UNDERWIRES should sit behind the breast tissue and not rub or dig in.

BRAS lose effectiveness with use so if you run three times a week or more for up to an hour, replace yours every eight to 12 months. ■

TRAINING

Our expert tips will help you from your first training session all the way to the finish line of your first race

15 TRAINING
ESSENTIALS

Arm yourself with some basic knowledge and you'll soon be training with confidence

Running isn't rocket science but figuring out a training strategy can seem just as tricky. How many miles should you run? What is VO₂ max again? And lactate threshold? The fact every runner is unique further complicates matters. So it's crucial to learn the quirks and requirements of our own bodies and play by their rules. Luckily, there are principles that apply to almost every runner — whether slow or fast, training for a marathon or for life. Conceived by coaches and employed by elites, these time-tested rules will help you stay motivated, avoid injuries and run strong year after year.

1 START WELL
This might be your first try at running, you could be a return visitor who's had a break, or you might be attempting to improve on what you already do. The less running you've done recently, the more you can expect to improve in the first 10 weeks. On the other hand, the less you've run lately, the more likely you are to hurt yourself by doing too much, too soon. That's why it's important to set two related goals as you start or restart your running programme — you need to maximise improvements, but also minimise injuries.

2 ALWAYS WARM UP
Don't confuse a little light stretching with a good warm-up. Stretching generally doesn't make you sweat or raise your heart rate, which is what you want. A proper warm-up begins with walking or running very slowly to ease your body into the session. Try walking briskly for five minutes, then break into your comfortable running pace. After you've finished running, resist the urge to stop. Instead, walk another five minutes to cool down more gradually. After you've cooled down is the best time for some static stretching — this is when your muscles are still warm and at their most pliable.

3 MAKE A PLAN
As for finding places to run, anywhere that's safe for walking is also fine for running. Off-road routes (parks, footpaths, playing fields) are better than busy streets, while soft surfaces (grass and dirt) are better than paved ones, but any choice is better than staying at home and not running. Map out the best courses in your immediate area. This will save you time and solve the 'place' issue, making it much more likely you'll execute your planned runs.

4 EAT RIGHT
Sports nutrition is a huge and important topic, but, in general, the rules for good nutrition and fluid consumption are pretty much the same for runners as for every other athlete. There are three areas of special interest to runners: (1) control your weight, as extra pounds will slow you down; (2) eat lightly after training and racing; (3) drink 250-500ml of water or a carbohydrate drink an hour before running, as dehydration can be a dangerous enemy.

5 DON'T OVERTRAIN
If you've improved by running 15 miles a week, you could be so much better by running 30, right? Not exactly. Kenneth Cooper, a giant in the fitness field, devised a simple formula for improving as a runner. Run two to three miles, three to five days a week. It's easier to remember as the F.I.T. formula: frequency (running at least every other day); intensity (keep at a comfortable pace); and time (about 30 minutes per run). It's important to run these efforts at an easy, steady pace. Think of yourself as the tortoise, not the hare. Make haste slowly.

6 FIND YOUR PACE
Keeping a comfortable pace may sound simple but pushing that little bit too hard is a problem most novice runners experience, with the result that many get overly ▶

fatigued and discouraged. As a guideline a comfortable pace is two to three minutes per mile slower than your optimum mile time. Or you can use a heart-rate monitor and run at 65 per cent of your working heart rate. Finally, as a low-tech alternative, just try listening to your breathing. If you aren't gasping for air, and you can talk while you're running, your pace is about right.

10 GO EASY

Most runs need to be easy. This is true whether you're a beginner or an elite athlete. Of course, the definition of easy varies hugely; an easy mile for an experienced runner would be impossible for many beginners. If you're a newbie, limit yourself to one hard day per week, running longer and slower, or shorter and faster, than normal.

7 DECODE PAIN

Runners get hurt. Most injuries are musculoskeletal, meaning it's possible to recover relatively rapidly — just so long as you take days off or other appropriate action. Many running injuries are self-inflicted, brought on by going too far, too fast, too soon or too often. Getting over an injury can be as simple as changing your routine. If you can't run steadily without pain, try mixing walking and running. If you can't run-walk, simply walk. If you can't walk, cycle. If you can't cycle, swim. As you recover, climb back up this fitness ladder until you can run again.

8 THE MILE TRIAL

Once you've started running you'll soon be asked what your best mile time is — so you might as well get used to testing it. Soon you'll be calculating your pace per mile on longer runs, but you should begin with a simple one-mile test run to find your starting point.

Think of this run as a pace test, not a race. Run at a pace that is beyond easy, but isn't a massive struggle, and count on improving your mile time as your fitness improves.

9 BE BALANCED

As running works mainly the legs, if you're seeking total-body fitness you need to supplement it with other types of exercise. These should aim to strengthen the muscles running neglects, and stretch those running tightens, which means strengthening your upper body and stretching your legs. Always stretch out post-run and also add a few classic upper body moves such as press-ups and chin-ups. Your muscles will be nicely warmed up after running so they'll have the greatest benefit then.

11 RECOVER

Your body uses easy/off days to repair muscle fibres, increase your ability to process nutrients and oxygen, build new blood cells and eliminate waste. If you don't give your body enough time to recover, sooner or later you it will break down. As a rule of thumb, put an easy day between hard workouts and ensure you take at least one full day off a week. During training, reduce your mileage by 15 to 20 per cent every fourth week, and if you find a certain week is particularly difficult, stay at that level until it becomes more comfortable.

12 EXPECT PEAKS AND PLATEAUS

Most of us see the greatest improvements early in our running careers but at some point improvements will slow, or stop. That's not necessarily a bad thing, it just means you've adapted to your training and you've climbed to a higher plateau. Try adding some hills, increasing the duration of your tempo run, or trying longer or faster repeats as new ways to intensify your training sessions

and advance towards a new level. However, if you are already training at a high intensity then a plateau may be an indicator that you simply need to have a rest.

13 REGULAR RUNNING

Ask a coach what the single most important factor is in training, and most will say consistency. You won't improve if you run only once a week, or if you repeatedly run hard for a week, then take the next week off. Better running comes from maintaining a minimum, even if that's 30 minutes, two or three days a week. Plan your 'down' months for times you know it'll be harder to run — winter weather, big projects, life changes, and so on.

14 PRACTISE PATIENCE

Whether you're a new runner or returning after a break, increase quantity and quality gradually. An increase in mileage or time of only 10 per cent a week is recommended. So say you put in 20 miles a week, including one long run and one speed session. You could add a mile to your long run and a half-mile to an easy run, while increasing your speed session by one 800m rep for a total of two additional miles across the whole week. Avoid increasing intensity and distance simultaneously. New runners should focus on going further before going faster.

15 BE A WINNER

One of the beauties of running is it gives everyone a chance to win. Unlike other sports, there's no need to beat an opponent or an arbitrary standard. Runners are able to measure themselves against their own standards. When you improve a time, increase a distance or set a personal best in a race, you win — no matter what anyone else has done on the same day. ∎

RUNNING ROUTE
Having a plan makes
achieving goals easier

MAKE A MASTER *PLAN*

How to schedule key training elements to become healthier, stronger and faster

B etween work, family and social obligations, life can sometimes feel like a game of Tetris – so many moving pieces and a limited amount of time to fit them into the right places. If you tell yourself you'll run whenever you have a free moment, you may rarely get out at all – and when you do, you won't be reaping the benefits of a more thought-out approach. 'A training plan gives you direction and structure,' says Mackenzie Madison, a professional triathlete and coach. 'It brings variety, too, so you're not doing the same thing every day.'

Variation has physical benefits as well. Research shows picking up the pace for short sections provides extra cardiovascular benefits and can aid weight loss. Adding weight training can help prevent injuries and improve bone density. Your training plan can keep you from overdoing it, since rest and hard efforts will be in balance. And it can give you confidence that you can bring to your next race.

Coaches and commercially available training plans are good ways to add structure to your routine, but a DIY approach can be very effective, too. If you follow a few basic guidelines you should be able to plan your own training or adjust an existing plan to fit your lifestyle.

WHEN LIFE *STRIKES*

Sometimes you just can't get out to run. Here's what to do if...

You have to miss a workout	**You have to miss two workouts**	**You were up all night with a sick child**	**You just simply can't find the time**
'If it's once in a while, let it go,' says running coach Jennifer Harrison. 'If you're consistently missing a key weekly workout, you need to reevaluate your schedule or your goals.'	'Reschedule the one that best aligns with your goal and skip the other,' says Harrison. For example, for if training for a marathon, prioritise your long run.	'If it's one night of no sleep you can probably complete your morning workout,' says Harrison. 'If it's several nights, skip it and sleep in.'	Harrison split her runs in half when her twins were babies (two 20-min runs instead of one 40-min session). Do what you can in the time you have.

Words **AC Shilton** Photography **Mitch Mandel**

1 PLOT THREE GOOD DAYS

'Three quality days a week is how much a person needs to run to improve,' says running coach Cliff Latham. 'If you're doing a long run one day, a tempo run another day and intervals on a third day, you'll see improvement.' And that doesn't just mean faster race times: these workouts ramp up calorie-burning, boost overall health and make you a more confident runner.

Long runs build endurance and mental toughness, and you don't have to go very far to benefit. Latham says that athletes who aren't training for a half marathon or longer can make eight miles their limit. Build your distance slowly, adding no more than a mile a week, and keep the pace easy. Many runners plan long runs for the weekend, when most of us have more time.

Busy weekdays are great for interval runs: a 2012 review of studies found interval training reduced the risk of high blood pressure, while a 2015 study found subjects who included bursts of speed kept burning calories at a higher-than-normal rate post-run. Intervals can last from 30 seconds to a mile, with periods of walking or jogging between 'on' periods. The effort should feel hard but not all-out – near 5K pace.

Tempo runs – sustained efforts at a comfortably hard pace – blend the endurance-boosting properties of long runs with the speed-developing benefits of intervals. Tempo runs train your body and brain to up the pace and keep it there.

If you choose to run on the other four days of the week, go at an easy pace.

2 BUILD IN BREAK TIMES

It's almost impossible to give a recommendation for how much rest you'll need. 'It depends on age, experience and whether you're injury-prone or not,' says Harrison. 'A good rule is don't run two hard days back to back.' (Long-run days count as hard days, despite the easy pace.)

Also, know that a rest day doesn't mean you have to be totally slothful. Harrison, who coaches triathletes, says some of her athletes swim on rest days. In a 2010 study, triathletes who swam after a hard interval run were able to run stronger than those who rested in a 'time to fatigue' test the next day. And don't worry if swimming isn't your thing – Latham's athletes practise other forms of active recovery, such as yoga, walking or going for a bike ride. But take at least one day a week completely off from exercise – two, if you're starting out, injury-prone or susceptible to mental burnout.

3 ALWAYS WARM UP (AND DOWN)

It can be tempting to jump right into your workout, but Madison says that's a bad idea. Your body needs at least 15 minutes to increase blood flow to major muscle groups. Plus a 2012 study found athletes who performed a dynamic warm-up had more hamstring flexibility and quad strength than those who didn't. Increased flexibility helps protect against injuries, especially during intervals or tempo pace runs. Consider starting workouts – especially hard ones – with jogging and plyometrics to activate key running muscles. Madison says that early morning runners in particular need warm-up time, since we move very little when we sleep. But coach Joe McConkey says evening runners aren't off the hook: 'You've been sitting all day, so you may need a longer warm-up – particularly before high-intensity work.' He has his athletes do 10-15 minutes of jogging plus a few drills and dynamic stretches (such as high knees) before beginning the fast portion of a workout.

Don't forget to cool down. 'When we're working hard, all systems are firing, but when we suddenly stop, these systems slam on the brakes without letting our bodies return to normal,' says Madison. Jog for a few minutes after a hard workout, then walk. Build in at least 10 minutes after interval or tempo runs, though Madison says you can use the final mile or two of a long or easy run to start the cool-down process.

4 SET ASIDE STRENGTH TIME

Madison's athletes do two hour-long strength-training sessions a week, plus three sessions of core training. (That can mean simply doing a few planks, leg lifts and crunches after a run.) She recommends dedicating one weight-training day to building power with drills and plyometrics – such as walking lunges and box jumps – while the other should be used to work on general body strength. Prioritise the core work. If you can fit in only one strength session a week, focus on power one week and strength and stability the next. Latham says that if you're truly time-starved, try fewer reps with heavy weights. Doing as few as four reps with the most weight you can manage builds strength quickly.

Timing is a matter of personal preference. If you do it after a tough workout, you can take the next day off. 'But, mentally, that can be hard,' says Latham. If the choice is doing it on your easy day or not doing it at all, do it on your easy day.

5 TAKE TIME TO RECOVER

To feel your best on all your runs, help your body to rebuild between sessions. 'Make sure you eat a protein-rich snack after you run,' says Madison, especially after hard workouts or runs lasting longer than an hour. Also, try to get enough sleep – however much you need to wake feeling rested – as well as time with your foam roller. 'Foam rolling works out the scar tissue we all have in our muscles, ' says Madison. Focus mainly on your lower body – the quads, hamstrings, calves, glutes and IT bands.

Harrison recommends rolling for 15-20 minutes a day. At a minimum, try to get in five minutes every day with longer sessions after tough workouts.

6 TRAIN TO RACE

If you're targeting a race, try to start most of your long runs at the time of day your race will begin. Harrison says you should do one or two dress rehearsal runs in the weeks leading up to the taper to test what you'll eat the day before the race, how you'll fuel and what you'll wear.

Your pace on these runs should mimic race day, at least for a few miles, says Madison. You'll learn a lot: for example,

prerun porridge might work for you on easy days, but if your stomach revolts when you speed up, you'll be glad to know that in advance.

When to start your taper is a personal choice, says McConkey. Some half and full marathoners taper for a few weeks, while 5K and 10K runners need less taper time. 'It should be shorter volume and more rest, but with the intensity still high,' says McConkey. Do fewer, shorter reps at your usual pace during speed sessions. Harrison has her athletes do only four reps 'so they can keep that snap and not exhaust their legs', she says. 'The key is to keep muscle memory and snap alive.'

COOL YOUR BOOTS
Walking after a hard run feels good and works wonders

WHEN TO WING IT

Your plan shouldn't own you. Bend the rules for these scenarios

Your friends go for a long run on a different day than you'd planned
Go, but stick to your pace if someone in the group opts to treat long-run day like tempo day.

There's a fun 5K you want to do at the last minute
'Do fun things when you can,' says coach Madison. 'Just know that one might jeopardise the next day of training.'

You missed a hard workout, so you do it the day before a long run
Learning how to run on tired legs can help you late in tough races, says coach Latham. But don't do this often.

You're exhausted
Building a schedule takes trial and error; you have to figure out how much rest you need. Listen to your body – not your smartphone's calendar alert.

IN THE LONG *RUN*

If you manage them right, your long runs will help you improve in covering the distance better, from 10K to marathons and beyond

'T' he long run is the single most important workout you can do,' says coach Jeff Galloway, who ran the 10,000m for the US in the 1972 Olympics, 'But it's more complex than you'd think, and most runners don't do it right.'

Here we answer the many questions about long runs, and look at related issues such as nutrition, rest and recovery.

WHY DO LONG RUNS?

■ To strengthen the heart.
■ They open up capillaries, speeding energy into working muscles and flushing away waste from tired ones.
■ To strengthen leg muscles and ligaments.
■ They recruit fast-twitch muscle fibres to assist slow-twitch tasks, for example marathon running.
■ To help burn fat as fuel.
■ They boost confidence. 'If you know you can go that far in training, it gives you the confidence that with the adrenaline of the race, you can do that too,' says Danielle Sanderson, former European 50K champion.
■ They can make you a lot faster. 'Increase your long run from six miles to 12 — change nothing else — and you will see an improvement in your 10K time,' says Galloway.

HOW LONG?

It's not an exact science but there are two general rules:

Time is a much better gauge than distance. 'The duration of the long run will vary depending on the athlete's age, fitness and the competitive distance they're training for,' explains Norman Brook, Britain's former national endurance coach. "The run should be for a minimum of 45 minutes and up to three hours for elite athletes and those preparing to run a marathon or ultra-distance events.'

The goal of a long run is not covering a certain distance, but quality time spent on your feet. You should gradually try to get your long-run time up to one-and-a-half to two hours. That's the minimum — roughly 10-16 miles — needed to maintain a high endurance level. Increase your long runs by no more than 15 minutes at a time. 'Build up to the long run gradually,' Brook advises. 'If the longest you're running for is 30 minutes, gradually build up to an hour by adding five minutes to your run each week.' Just a few minutes of extra running makes a difference — do too much and you could find yourself injured.

HOW FAST?

You want to run a marathon in 3:30, which is eight-minute-mile pace, so obviously you do your long runs at that pace. 'Running isn't always logical,' says Benji Durden, a 2:09 marathoner who now coaches both elite and recreational runners. There are reasons for going easy on your 20-milers:
■ Long runs at race pace may be training sessions in your mind, but they're races to your body. That can lead to overtraining, injury or illness. 'Running long runs fast causes more problems than any other mistake,' says Galloway. Marian Sutton, winner of many marathons, agrees: 'There's no point pushing yourself too hard. You need to run at a pace that feels comfortable.'
■ Fast, long runs miss the point. 'Long runs are for endurance,' says Sanderson.

> ## THE LONG RUN IS THE MOST IMPORTANT WORKOUT YOU CAN DO, BUT IT'S MORE COMPLEX THAN YOU THINK

'It's amazing how quickly they reduce your resting heart rate, making your heart more efficient.'
■ The ideal pace for long runs is at least one minute per mile slower than your marathon pace. 'The intensity of effort is low, and you should ensure a steady state is maintained,' says Brook. 'You should be able to conduct a conversation while you're running.'
■ You might even walk at points during

Illustration **Thomas Fuchs**

GO THE DISTANCE
Long runs aren't
just for endurance

longer runs – it works for Sanderson. 'It's good to just plod round, walk a bit if you need to, or even stop for a break,' she advises.

HOW OFTEN?

Don't run long more than once a week. It is, after all, a hard session, requiring rest or easy days before and after. The other end of the scale is debatable. Some runners have no problem going two or three weeks between long runs. Others will come back with a midweek long run if a shorter race precludes the weekend session. Galloway recommends a simple formula: roughly one day's gap per mile of your long run. For example, if your long run is 12-17 miles, you can go two weeks between long runs without losing endurance; if it's 18-23 miles, three weeks, 'If you're running at least 30 minutes every other day in between,' he adds. This can also be used to taper before a marathon. For instance, if your last long run is 22 miles, you'd run it three weeks before race day. If it's 16 miles, you get a two-week rest before the race.

WHICH DAY?

Sunday is traditional, because that's when most people have most free time. Also, most marathons are at weekends. But there's no need to stick to a set day. 'I'm not rigid about it,' says marathon world record holder Paula Radcliffe, 'because I never know when I'll be racing.' Sanderson also plans her schedule around events. 'I do my long run on a Sunday, unless I'm racing,' she says.

AREN'T THEY BORING?

Contrary to popular opinion, long runs aren't dull and tedious. You just have to know how to run them – that is, with friends. Find a Saturday or Sunday morning group, or arrange to meet a training partner regularly. 'I do some of my runs with friends,' says Sanderson, 'and the time always goes much faster.' ∎

PERFECT
TEMPO

The 'comfortably hard' run is the key to clocking
your fastest time. Here's how to make it work for you

Pssst! Want to run like a world-beater? OK, you might not make it to the very top, but your training regime can help you achieve new PBs, simply by incorporating the same method that helped propel the likes of Ethopian world-record holder, Haile Gebrselassie, and his Kenyan predecessor, Paul Tergat, to running greatness.

The secret? The tempo run, that faster-paced session, also known as a lactate-threshold, LT or threshold run. One US-based coach championing this

method is Toby Tanser. In 1995, when Tanser was an elite track runner for Sweden, he trained with the Kenya 'A' team for seven months. They ran classic tempos — a slow 15-minute warm-up, followed by at least 20 minutes at a challenging but manageable pace, then a 15-minute cool-down — as often as twice a week. 'The foundation of Kenyan running is based almost exclusively on tempo training,' says Tanser. 'It changed my view on training.'

Today, Tanser and many other running experts believe

that tempo runs are the single most important session you can do to improve your speed for any race distance. 'There's no beating the long run for pure endurance,' says Tanser. 'But tempo running is crucial to racing success because it trains your body to sustain speed over distance.' So crucial, in fact, that it trumps track sessions in the longer distances. 'Tempo training is more important than speedwork for the half and full marathon,' says Gale Bernhardt, author of *Training Plans for*

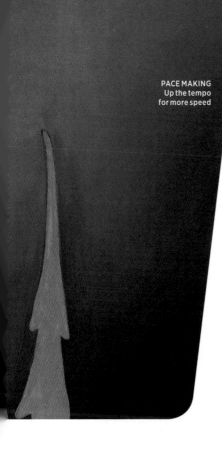

PACE MAKING
Up the tempo
for more speed

Multisport Athletes. 'Everyone who does tempo runs diligently will improve.' However, you also have to be diligent about getting out and doing them.

WHY IT WORKS

Tempo running improves a crucial physiological variable for running success: metabolic fitness. Most runners train their cardio system to better deliver oxygen to the muscles, but not how to use it once it arrives. Tempo runs teach the body to use the oxygen for metabolism more efficiently.

How? By increasing your lactate threshold (LT), or the point at which the body fatigues at a certain pace. 'During tempo runs, lactate and hydrogen ions, by-products of metabolism, are released into the muscles,' says Dr Carwyn Sharp, chief science officer at the NSCA. The ions make the muscles acidic, eventually leading to fatigue. The better trained you become, the higher you push your threshold, meaning your muscles become better at using these by-products. The result is less acidic muscles — in other words, muscles that haven't reached their new threshold,

so they keep on contracting, allowing you to run further and faster.

DOING IT PROPERLY

But you've got to put in enough time at the right intensity — it's easy to get it wrong with runs that are too short and too slow. 'You need to get the hydrogen ions in the muscles for a sufficient length of time for the muscles to become adept at using them,' says Sharp. Typically, 20 minutes is sufficient, or two to three miles if your goal is general fitness or a 5K. Runners tackling longer distances should do longer tempo runs during their peak training weeks: four to six miles for the 10K, six to eight for the half-marathon and eight to 10 for a full marathon.

HOW SHOULD IT FEEL?

It should feel what we call "comfortably hard". You know you're working, but you're not racing. At the same time, you'd be happy if you could slow down. You'll be even happier if you make tempo running a part of your training schedule, and get results that make you feel like a champion. ∎

GETTING YOUR TEMPO *RIGHT*

A classic tempo run is a sustained, hard effort for two to four miles, with a decent warm-up and cool-down

GOAL: Get Started
Coach Gale Bernhardt uses this four-week progression for tempo newbies. Warm-up and cool-down for 10-15 minutes.

Week 1 5x3 minutes at tempo pace, 60-second easy jog after each one (if you find that you have to walk during the recovery, you're going too hard).
Week 2 5x4 minutes at tempo pace, 60-second easy jog recovery.
Week 3 4x5 minutes at tempo pace, 90-second easy jog recovery.

Week 4 20 minutes steady tempo pace.

GOAL: 5K to 10K
Run three easy miles, followed by two repeats of two miles at 10K pace or one mile at 5K pace. Recover with one mile easy between repeats. Do a two-mile easy cool-down for a total distance of eight or 10 miles.

GOAL: Half to Full Marathon
Do this challenging long run once or twice during training. After a warm-up, run three (half-marathoners)

or six (marathoners) miles at the easier end of your tempo pace range. Jog for five minutes, and then do another three or six miles. 'Maintaining that pace for so many miles will whip you into shape for longer distances,' says Tanser.

THE RIGHT RHYTHM
To ensure you're running at the right pace, use one of these four methods to help to gauge your intensity:

RECENT RACE
Add 30-40 seconds per kilometre to your current

5K pace or 15-20 seconds to your current 10K pace.

HEART RATE
Run at 85-90 per cent of your maximum heart rate (use a heart-rate monitor to maintain this).

PERCEIVED EXERTION
An eight on a one to 10 scale (a comfortable effort would be five; racing close to a 10).

TALK TEST
A few words should be possible, but if you're having a conversation you're going too slow.

TIME TO GIVE PACE A *CHANCE*

Even if speed isn't your main focus, fast workouts can benefit every runner, no matter what your goals may be

Think speedwork is just for front-of-the-packers with time goals? Think again. Research suggests that 30-second to five-minute bursts of intense exercise interspersed with rest periods will yield great physiological changes – such as better blood sugar control and improved blood vessel function – that slow runs just can't deliver as efficiently. 'When it comes to these benefits, interval training is at least equal to steady runs,' says exercise scientist Jonathan Little, an assistant professor at the University of British Columbia in Canada.

The there's the increased range of movement in your joints and improvement in ability to pace yourself. Speedwork can also make your runs feel easier, improve your form and foster mental toughness, says coach Greg McMillan.

'I'M RUNNING MY FIRST 5K, SO I DON'T REALLY NEED *SPEEDWORK*'

The shorter the distance, the more important speedwork is, and the more frequently you should do it, says McMillan. Whether you have a time goal or not, the improved blood sugar, cardiovascular fitness and mental toughness gained will make your 5K feel easier. And if you want to run a fast 5K, short bursts will improve your aerobic power.

THE WORKOUT
You can do speedwork more often than runners targeting longer races (perhaps twice a week), mix it up. Try a time-based fartlek session: at the end of a run, speed up for four minutes; jog for two; run fast for four minutes; jog for two; run fast for three minutes; jog for two; run fast for one. Or try hill repeats – do a 10-minute warm-up jog to a hill that will take you 45 seconds to climb. Run up at a comfortably hard pace. Walk down. Do 8-10 reps.

'I RUN TO IMPROVE MY HEALTH, NOT TO COMPETE IN *RACES*'

Skeletal muscle is critical for soaking up glucose from food and keeping your blood sugar levels in check. Because intense interval training engages a broader range of muscle fibres, it creates a bigger internal 'sponge', helping to fend off diabetes, says Little. It also strengthens the heart muscle and blood vessels and increases the number of mitochondria (the fuel-burning engines in your muscles), making your body more efficient at metabolising fuel. The result: you will have more energy – for running and for doing everything else.

THE WORKOUT
Warm up for 15 minutes. Run one minute at 10K pace (this should be a 7-8 on an exertion scale of 1-10). Walk or jog for one minute, then repeat. Start with 4-6 reps. Build to 10 reps.

'I WANT TO LOSE WEIGHT, SO I RUN CONSISTENTLY, NOT *FAST*'

'The faster you run, the more calories you expend,' says Adam St Pierre, an exercise physiologist with Boulder Center for Sports Medicine, US. Research suggests that interval training also prompts the body to burn more calories in the hours after exercise. It shouldn't replace moderate running, says St Pierre, but a weekly speed session utilises different muscles, potentially reducing your injury risk (provided you ease into speedwork and build duration and intensity gradually).

THE WORKOUT
For weight loss, the longer the period of intensity, the better. Warm up, then run at 10K pace for 3-5 mins. Then jog or walk for 3-5 mins. Repeat 6-10 times. Or set the treadmill gradient to five per cent and run at a moderate pace for 3 mins. Lower to zero and keep the same pace for 3 mins. Repeat 6-10 times.

GO FOR FULL **RECOVERY**

When to walk, jog or push the pace between speed intervals

Your instinct may be to stop to catch your breath between reps, but jogging can make it easier to run fast in the next interval. It keeps more blood flowing through your legs, clearing the metabolic waste products that build up during hard running. However, walking allows muscle phosphocreatine – the energy that fuels bursts of effort – to recharge properly. Your choice depends on what you want from a session.

WHEN TO JOG

British researchers recently tracked the lactate levels of cyclists during 'active' and 'passive' recovery. Active recovery – the equivalent of jogging – caused lactate to drop after about 90 secs, but offered no advantage if the period was shorter.

Jogging is best between reps lasting 3-5 mins. Reps such as 4x1200m at 5K pace, with 3-4 mins rest, will leave your legs heavy. Jogging will flush them out leaving you ready.

WHEN TO WALK

Given that lactate clearance is enhanced after about 90 secs, it's tempting to walk for shorter recoveries. But jogging increases aerobic demands, so it's ideal during base-building phases.

Recover by walking when you're doing short intervals to work on your top speed, in which case starting with full phosphocreatine stores gives you an edge. For a workout such as 6x200m, with two minutes' rest, walk the whole recovery.

WHEN TO PUSH IT

Full and half marathoners can try intervals just faster than threshold pace, with recoveries slightly slower than threshold. They teach your body to move lactate out of the muscles and into the bloodstream, where it's reused as fuel.

Try this: 4x5 minutes at 10 seconds per mile faster than half-marathon pace, recovering with 5 minutes at 10-15 seconds slower than marathon pace. Do this during a marathon build-up.

'I'M RUNNING A MARATHON, SO I WANT TO BUILD **DISTANCE**'

Near the end of a marathon, many first-timers run out of fuel and their form falls apart. Fast repeats teach your body what it feels like to have a light, quick turnover – a biomechanical efficiency applicable to any speed or distance, says St Pierre. Quick repeats also strengthen fast-twitch muscles so they can be used when other muscles are trashed, he adds. Plus they'll improve overall running economy.

THE WORKOUT

Start with 6-10 200m repeats at a 5K pace, with a 200m jog in-between. Do this once a week. Over time, increase the distance (eg 5x400m at 5-10K pace, or 4x600m at 10K pace). Your total mileage at a fast pace shouldn't exceed 10 per cent of your weekly total. Running 20 miles per week? Run no more than two miles hard in speedwork. ∎

20 WAYS TO *SPEED*

These tips will make you faster, especially when you want to kick for home at the end of a race

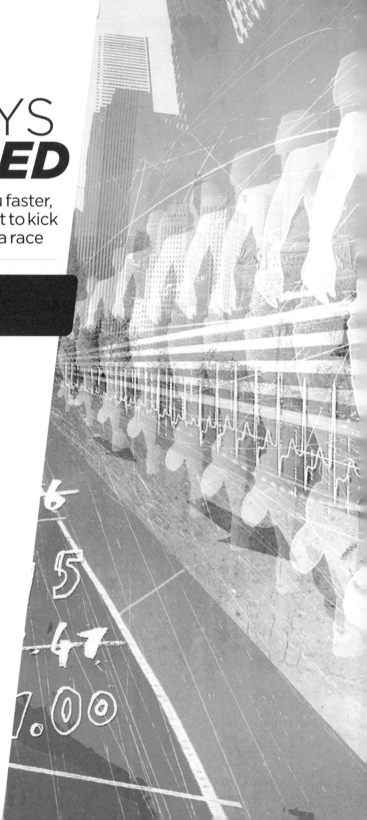

1 KEEP IT SHORT
You could start with a session of brisk efforts. Six minutes brisk, one-minute walk, six minutes brisk and so on.

2 ADD SOME FARTLEK TRAINING
To begin, add some quick bursts into your shorter runs. Each burst can be as little as 20 seconds or as much as a few minutes.

3 DO AN INTERVAL SESSION
6 x 1 minute, with three-minute jog/walk recoveries, or 5x2 minutes with five-minute jogs.

4 GO FOR SHORT REPS
After two months or so of speedwork, try your first session of short repetitions: 5 x 300m, with four-minute recoveries; 5 x 200m, with 3-minute rests; or try 10 x 200m with 3-minute recoveries.

5 GLIDE DOWNHILL
On down slopes during long runs, go with the hill and allow it to pick up your pace to around 80-85 per cent of flat-out, allowing gravity to power you downhill. Don't go any further than 150m. The idea is to speed up without using any extra energy.

Illustration **Andy Potts**

6 DO A PYRAMID SESSION

Start at 120m, add 20m to each rep until you reach 200m, then come back down to 120m. Run these at 400m pace, with a walk-back recovery.

7 TRY FAST REPS

For 200m or 300m: run 6-10 x 200m, with three-minute recoveries, or 5-8 x 300m, with five-minute recoveries. Start both at 800m pace, eventually running the last reps flat out.

8 DO A SIMULATION SESSION

This should replicate an 800m race. Run two sets of either 500m + 300m, or 600m + 200m, at your target 800m pace.

9 BUILD YOURSELF UP

Find an open area and mark out a circuit of 800-1,000m. Run a circuit at your 5K pace, jog for five minutes, then run a second circuit, aiming to do it about three seconds faster than the last. Speed up by three seconds until you've done five circuits.

10 KEEP GOING

Now try 5 x 800m at a pace 10 seconds faster per 800m than your usual 5K pace. Recover between intervals for the same amount of time it takes you to run them.

11 PILE ON THE MILES

Begin with a three-mile warm-up, then 4 x 1 mile at a pace faster than your 10K pace, with a three-minute jog between each.

12 BUILD YOUR PYRAMIDS

Try 1,000m, 2,000m, 3,000m, 2,000m, 1,000m at your half-marathon race pace, with a four-minute recovery between each.

13 OR DO A HALF PYRAMID

If you're short on time, try 400m, 800m, 1,200m, 1,600m, 2,000m, each run faster than your 10K pace but not flat out. Jog 400m between.

14 CARVE UP A 2K SPEED SESSION

Divide 2,000m into: 400m at 5K race pace, with a 400m jog; 300m at race pace, with a 300m jog; 200m slightly quicker than race pace, with a 200m jog; 100m slightly quicker, with a 100m jog.

15 GO LONGER

Run five miles, alternating three-minute bursts at 10K pace with 90-second recoveries.

16 GO OFF-ROAD...

Jog for 10 minutes, then run at your mile pace for 1:40; slow down to a jog (don't walk) and recover for three minutes, then repeat another 100-second burst. Try four of these sessions to begin with, and gradually work up to doing 10 altogether.

17 ...OR USE A TRACK

Run eight laps, alternating fast and slow 200s. The fast 200s should be hard, but not a full sprint.

18 BUILD UP TO 5K

Break it down into 5 x 1,000m. Run 800m at your 10K race pace, then accelerate to 3K pace for the last 200m, with three-minute recoveries.

19 BREAK UP THE LONGER RUNS

Run at your marathon pace for five minutes, then increase your speed to 10K pace for one minute. Continue this for 30 minutes.

20 DIVIDE YOUR TIME

If you want to complete a marathon in three hours 27 minutes, run 800m reps in three minutes and 27 seconds. ■

WHERE THERE'S A HILL, THERE'S A *WAY*

How to power up, over and down any incline

Australian middle-distance runner Herb Elliott often included sand-dune workouts in his training. In 1960 he took Olympic gold in the 1500m, beating his own world record. His achievements helped establish hill running as part of many training plans. But simply sprinting up and down inclines isn't a winning strategy, as Australian researchers discovered. The experts wired up a group of runners to monitor speed, oxygen consumption, heart rate and stride length, then sent them out for a six-mile time trial over a hilly course. They found that runners poorly judged their effort over hilly terrain, ascended too fast and took more than a minute to recover. Don't make the same mistakes – here's what you should be doing:

ON THE WAY **UP** ⚏

On hills, you must maintain an even effort – equivalent to your effort on flats, and sustainable the whole way up – or you risk burning energy you can't regain later on. Most runners in the study did just that: they went too fast on climbs, causing their breathing and heart rate to spike as if they were sprinting.

DO IT RIGHT Once or twice a week, practise running long hills to develop your ability to lock into a sustainable pace. Aim for ascents that take 10 minutes or longer. Mimic the effort you'd expend on a flat run, no matter how slow it feels. Listen to your breathing; if it gets noticeably heavier, ease up.

Words **Alex Hutchinson** Illustration **Frank Stockton**

UP AGAINST IT
Patience and good
technique will help
your conquer hills

CRESTING THE **TOP**

After reaching the top of a hill, the runners took an average of 78 seconds before they sped up to their normal pace. That's partly because they were going too fast up the hill and partly because the hills shortened their stride rhythm. It's natural to maintain that shorter stride until you've recovered and it takes a conscious effort to snap out of it.

DO IT RIGHT **Use 'long strides' as a cue to open up your stride and accelerate. To practise making this transition find a hill that takes about 45 seconds to climb. Run hard to the top, then lengthen your stride and accelerate for 15 seconds to drive home the quick transition. Jog down for recovery. Repeat six to 10 times.**

COMING **DOWN**

Some people are better at downhills than others. While all the runners slowed on uphills — by an average of 23 per cent — they sped up on the way down by five to 25 per cent. If you don't practise, you'll end up braking on descents simply because you're not used to the pounding.

DO IT RIGHT **Good form is essential if you want to use gravity to your advantage. After a run, do four to six relaxed 100m strides down a gentle slope; progress over time to a steeper decline. Keep your arms wide and low for balance, shorten your stride and focus on quick steps. If your breathing gets quieter and slower, you can push harder without any penalty.** ■

HIGHER, FASTER, **STRONGER!**

Add one of these workouts to your weekly programme

SUPER-STEADY TEMPO
Run for 20-30 mins at tempo effort, focusing on maintaining a regular, controlled breathing pattern when you're tackling the hills.

SLOPE FARTLEK
Run for 30 mins, pushing hard uphill and downhill; push for an extra 10 secs after each climb and descent. Run easy on the flats to recover.

MAKING GOOD
PROGRESS

Progression runs are a great way to build strength, speed and toughness – and there is a multitude of variations to fit every goal

A decade ago, progression runs were considered a Kenyan training secret. Today, they're no longer restricted to fleet-footed east Africans: many runners and coaches use them. But how and when to run them is often unclear. The name 'progression run' designates only that the run advances from a slower to a faster pace. It can have one gear change or many; it can be a sub-threshold workout or an intense, faster-than-race-pace workout, or both in the same run. That variability is part of the value, making progression runs a versatile tool in a runner's box of workouts. Also valuable is the fact that you work various paces and systems in the same routine and needn't know your specific threshold or VO$_2$ max pace. But runners need some guidelines on what pace and distance to run. The following are a few favourite progression runs from top coaches and athletes, which you can adapt for any training plan.

USEFUL TOOL
A progression run can help increase your speed

MEDIUM-TO-HARD LONG RUN

FROM: Ryan Hall, sub-2:05 marathoner, US Olympian.

THE RUN: Start with one hour to 70 minutes at a medium effort (approximately a minute slower than marathon pace), then go into 50-60 minutes of hard running at around marathon pace.

WHEN: As a marathon simulation, mid-to-late in a training programme.

COACH'S NOTES: 'This is a hard run for me. After a warm-up and cool-down I will have covered between 20-26 miles, most at a very high level. I like this run because it teaches my body to run its fastest at the end of a long run when my legs are already tired.'

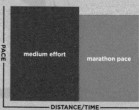

PACE

medium effort | marathon pace

DISTANCE/TIME

60-70 min | 50-60 min

5K PACE CUTDOWN

FROM: Micah Porter, coach.
THE RUN: During a 45-minute run, do the first 15 minutes 50 per cent slower than race pace, then 13 minutes at 25 per cent slower, 10 minutes at race pace, and seven minutes faster.
WHEN: Primarily early in the year, with some athletes running these throughout in place of structured intervals.
COACH'S NOTES: 'For athletes who have set down a good aerobic base through the winter, progression runs test their endurance, strength and aerobic limits. My runners find it hard to run the last seven minutes; but it's crucial in improving lactic threshold.'

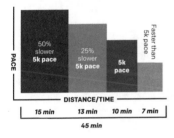

OUT-AND-BACK TEMPO

FROM: Trina Painter, coach based in Flagstaff, Arizona, US.
THE RUN: Run out for 10-20 minutes easy. Turn around and return two to five minutes faster at threshold pace.
WHEN: A few times before a 5K.
COACH'S NOTES: 'The goal is a moderate, less-than-race-pace effort; comfortably hard, with runners able to hold one-word conversations. Those who turn sooner take the lead and try not to get caught by the other groups. Running on the front changes the mental focus of some runners, and they surprise themselves by how well they run to stay up front as compared to feeling like they're hanging on.'

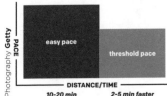

Photography **Getty**

STEADY TEMPO DROP

FROM: Layne Anderson, coach of Olympic marathon runner Diane Nukuri-Johnson.
THE RUN: A nine-mile progression run with a rise in pace, approximately five seconds per mile, until the last 1.5 miles at half marathon pace.
WHEN: Later training schedule.
COACH'S NOTES: 'Progression runs give good, controlled volume and prime the pump at the end with some fast-relaxed running. They're also easily tailored to the level of groups and can be adapted for specific distances. I get a lot of good feedback and they're a great confidence booster.'

CHAMPION'S FINISH
Moses Tanui, 10,000m gold medallist

LONG RUN CUT-DOWN

FROM: Pete Pfitzinger, 2:11 marathoner and author.
THE RUN: 20-23 miles. Start easy and slowly increase the pace to a minute-per-mile faster by 10 miles and another 30 seconds by 15 miles. Finish at close to marathon pace.
WHEN: Alternate weeks for the last 12 weeks of marathon training.
COACH'S NOTES: 'We had an outstanding group training in Wellesley in the mid-to-late 1980s. None of this was planned, unless one of the marathoners had to put in a hard session. Our loops were out and back, and the sense we were heading home stimulated the effort.'

FAST-FINISH LONG RUNS

FROM: Greg McMillan, coach and physiologist (the workout was learned from Gabriele Rosa, coach of Moses Tanui and other Kenyan champions).
THE RUN: Start at your normal long easy-run pace, one to two minutes slower than your marathon pace. Six miles from the end of the run, increase to your marathon pace. During the last two miles, increase the pace to end with an all-out 400m finish.
WHEN: Three to four times every other week towards the end of your marathon training. Make sure you've got several steady long runs under your belt before adding it on.
COACH'S NOTES: 'The last 10-30 minutes of the fast-finish are like a race. You run as hard as you can and sprint at the end. It's gruelling but race-specific training.' ∎

OUTSIDE IN
Running indoors
doesn't have to
be a chore

THE UPSIDE OF RUNNING *INSIDE*

Whether you're a convert or a sceptic, here's how to get the most out of your time on the mill

The treadmill can be more than a stopgap on days when the weather doesn't cooperate or the baby is taking a nap upstairs. Done right, treadmill training will help you maintain and improve your fitness throughout the winter so you're ready to race — or outpace your running buddies — by the time spring comes along.

'If you're doing a spring marathon like London, the treadmill gives you the option to take some of your training away from the cold of the British winter,' says running coach Nick Anderson (runningwithus.com).

On top of a friendlier temperature, you can tackle made-to-order hills and enjoy cushioning that protects your joints. Most importantly, you force yourself to stick to a pace. 'You've got to keep up, or you'll fly off the back of the machine,' says Rick Morris, author of *Treadmill Training for Runners* (£12.19, amazon.co.uk).

It may take a little experimenting to build a routine you enjoy. That's fine — just don't make it too much of a routine. 'Be playful with your workouts,' says Gregory Florez, CEO of Fitadvisor. com. 'One day do a steady run, the next do intervals. Never get locked into the same pattern, otherwise your body will quickly adapt and you won't get as much out of your training.'

We've put together five workouts over the following pages that make the best use of a treadmill's multiple programme features and can be slotted into your current training programme. ▶

DREAD THE *MILL?*

Nine reasons to take your training indoors

1 It's the only way to do a tempo run on a cold, sleety morning without cursing your very existence.

2 There's no need to obsess over your mile splits because the belt demands an even pace. You just can't get it wrong.

3 You can condition your legs to get used to running up a variety of different inclines, even if you live in Suffolk.

4 There's no more rushing out the door trying to squeeze in an evening run before it gets too dark.

5 You get to do less layering, less shivering and less laundry.

6 You don't have to push a 20kg baby jogger up steep hills.

7 You can do hill repeats without having to look for suitable gradients – or pound down the other side of them, for that matter.

8 A cushioned treadmill belt is kinder to your body if you're recovering from an injury.

9 It's the only time you'll ever watch an *EastEnders* omnibus.

1 RACE **SIMULATIONS**

DO IT TO Train for the race course

Wouldn't it be great if you could train for the hills you'll encounter in your upcoming race? You can: it's possible to get an elevation chart for many races so you can simulate its topography.

THE WORKOUT
Mimic the course by using the race's elevation map to replicate your ups and downs on the treadmill. For instance, say you know there's a killer hill two-thirds of the way into a 10K you've entered. All you have to do is hit the 'up' button at the same point in your treadmill run.

INSIDE SCOOP
On race day, when you get to that killer hill, you can approach it with confidence, secure in the knowledge that you've done it before.

2 RANDOM **INTERVALS**

DO IT TO Mix things up

Unpredictable changes in incline and speed provide a more complete workout than a steady pace on a flat surface because they force you to work different muscles.

THE WORKOUT
Just a little variation in your run helps the time go by much faster. Try a 10-minute warm-up, 20 minutes of random intervals and a 10-minute cool-down.

INSIDE SCOOP
If you don't have much time, this will give you a burst of intensity over a short period. Plus, it's a healthy change for obsessive runners who like to plot out every split.

FATIGUE SLOWS EVERYONE DOWN. BUT ON THE TREADMILL YOU CAN ONLY SLOW DOWN WHEN THE BELT DOES

3 SPEED **INTERVALS**

DO IT TO Get faster

Most people slow down during intervals because they're fatigued. 'On the treadmill, you can only slow down when the belt does,' says Morris.

THE WORKOUT
Try three sets of three minutes at about 10 seconds per mile faster than 5K pace. It takes the treadmill a few seconds to get to your interval speed, so start timing once you've

reached it. Do two minutes of easy jogging inbetween each rep. Add another set every two weeks.

INSIDE SCOOP
It's a killer, but the results will definitely show.

4 TV TEMPO **RUN**

DO IT TO Lock in your pace

Tempo runs are hard to get right especially for inexperienced runners. Once you've entered your target pace, the treadmill ensures you stay at the right speed.

THE WORKOUT
Find a treadmill at the gym with a TV attached and tune in to ITV 10 minutes before your favourite half-hour programme. Do a 10-minute warm-up, and move up to your tempo pace when the episode begins. Jog during the

adverts, then resume your faster pace when the programme comes back on. Cool down for five minutes.

INSIDE SCOOP
As you improve, try maintaining your tempo pace throughout.

5 HILL **REPEATS**

DO IT TO Design your own terrain

You can control the gradient, and you don't have to run and place more stress on your quads. Instead, flatten the belt for a few minutes of recovery, then go back at it.

THE WORKOUT
Try one-minute runs up a four per cent incline with two minutes of slow, flat jogging in between. Build up to 10 reps at six per cent. This gives you a cardiovascular challenge but is easier on your legs.

INSIDE SCOOP
'You're doing the same intensity as you would be if you were running on a track, but on a track your legs have to move much faster,' says US Olympic marathoner Magdalena Lewy-Boulet.

TREAD **RIGHTLY**

Expert advice for those new to belting it out

Treadmills offer some benefits you may not get from the roads — as long as you adapt your workouts to match the conditions.

1 **ADJUST AS YOU GO**
Whenever Olympic marathoner Magdalena Lewy-Boulet uses the treadmill, she whacks the elevation up by two per cent to counter the lack of wind resistance she would face outside. Because there's no hard science equating wind resistance to incline percentages, experiment with your own adjustments.

2 **SHORTEN YOUR STRIDE**
While the constantly moving surface and extra cushioning of a treadmill has its benefits, it also makes most people adopt a shorter stride. 'It's kind of like running on grass instead of a nice firm surface where you generate a lot of power,' says Rick Morris. Listen to your body to find a comfortable pace. If your normal easy outdoor pace feels hard on a treadmill, slow it down.

3 **DRINK UP**
Due to the lack of circulating air you're likely to sweat more on a treadmill. To avoid dehydration, drink two to four sips of water every 15 minutes while you're running indoors. ∎

ALL-TERRAIN
TRAINING

How switching some of your quality workouts to trails and sand will build your stamina, strength, balance and mental toughness

SAND

Percy Cerutty, coach of Australia's 1960 Olympic 1500m winner Herb Elliott, favoured sand-dune workouts for building speed, strength and endurance. At Cerutty's seaside base, Elliott would sprint up a dune as many as 50 times in a row. The result: he retired never having lost a mile or 1500m race. Many runners have used dune workouts since then, including Steve Ovett (who ran at Merthyr Mawr, on the coast of Wales) and American 5K record holder Molly Huddle, who tested herself on the shores of Lake Michigan, in the northern US.

A DIFFERENT DUNE
Running on loose, dry sand takes 20-60 per cent more energy than running on grass. Plus, soft sand absorbs some of the energy from your foot strike instead of pushing you forward, and forces you to activate more muscles in your lower leg to stay upright. The result is levels of lactate – a marker of anaerobic fatigue – that spike two or three times

higher than on firm surfaces. One study found athletes improved VO_2 max by 10 per cent after eight weeks of sand workouts twice a week, compared with just six per cent for those doing the same workouts on grass.

Loose sand's other perk is its low impact forces, which result in less muscle damage. Physiology aside, one of the best reasons to hit the dunes is the workout in mental toughness it will give you.

LIFE'S A BEACH
Cerutty used three key dune circuits for workouts. The short circuit was a steep climb of just 25m, but with a 60-degree incline. To replicate this, try 10 reps of a hill that takes about 15 seconds to climb; walk or jog down for recovery, taking enough time that you're ready to sprint hard again on the next rep. Cerutty's mid-length circuit was about 400m, finishing at the top of a steep hill. For this kind of workout, start with six reps, and take at least two minutes' recovery. Finally, the longest circuit was a rolling loop of just over a mile up and down the dunes. Start with three reps and take

three minutes' recovery. If you have regular access to dunes, include a hill workout once a week during base training. If you have to travel to get to dunes, make the effort worth your while; pick a medium-length incline that takes 45-90 seconds to climb, to strike a balance between strength and endurance. See how many reps you can do (then feel free to take a few days to recover).

SHIFTING SANDS
It's hard to maintain good form when your feet keep sliding backwards. For a more powerful stride, push hard off your back foot (even though it's slipping) rather than reaching forward with your front. The soft surface may put extra strain on your Achilles tendon, so avoid sand workouts if you have a history of Achilles problems and stop if you feel any pain in your calf muscles. The other big issue to consider is whether or not to wear shoes, and there's no right answer. If you leave them on, wear tall socks to keep sand out. If you take them off, your foot and ankle muscles will work extra hard, so keep the first few workouts short. ➤

Photography **Kat Pisiolek for Hearst Studios**

NEW GROUND
Different surfaces
can give you
different gains

TOUGHER MUD
An unforgiving
surface can change
your workout

TRAIL

Runners usually think of trails as a nice place for an easy run – soft surfaces, birdsong and so on – and reserve hard workouts for the track or the roads. After all, how are you supposed to hit your goal pace with all those rocks and roots? But what doesn't trip you up makes you stronger - learning to run fast on uneven terrain has benefits that will translate to any surface. You'll build power, improve balance and hone your inner sense of pace – not to mention improve your motor skills and mental strength.

TRAIL MIX
Moving an interval workout from the track (pace-based) to the trail (time- and effort-based) couldn't be easier – and it can be just as varied. Every other week, do a series of out-and-back repeats (try 6x3 minutes with 90 seconds' rest). Pick a starting point and mark it; run hard for three minutes, then mark your end point. Rest, then run back, trying to make it past the point where you began; mark this new spot and – you guessed it – try and run further the next time. And every time after that.
To maintain a quick pace on trails, where sharp turns and other obstacles break your rhythm, avoid slowing down until the last moment and speed up again as soon as you can. Refine these acceleration and deceleration skills by running pace-change sprints after an easy run once a week. Find a field or path about 100m long and divide it by marking spots at the 30m and 70m point. Run medium-hard for the first section, hard for the second section, and medium-hard for the third section; walk back. Then run hard/medium-hard/hard. Do six in total and focus on shifting gears precisely when you pass the marker.

DRILL BITS
Runners are great at going forward but they're not so good at moving side to side – that's a problem when you're navigating switchbacks. Work on your strength, balance and range of motion by including some drills after your run twice a week. Try sideways skipping for 20-30m in both directions, 10 reps each of sideways lunges and lateral hops (jumping side to side on one foot at a time), and balancing on one foot for 20 seconds at a time. Strengthening these muscles and ingraining these movement patterns will enable you to flow around obstacles with ease.

SCOUT THE COURSE
Racing on trails puts your more than just your physical skills to the test, you've got to run a strategic race too. You can pace yourself well only if you know what to expect. Run the course in advance, if possible, or study the course map to be familiar with the terrain. It can be difficult to pass others on single-track trails, so work out where choke points will occur. If you're feeling good, surge about a half mile before bottlenecks to avoid getting stuck. And even if you're not feeling too good, surge anyway – in a trail race, sometimes a change of rhythm could be exactly what you need. ∎

CROSS
ROADS

Adding different disciplines to your regime can greatly improve your running

Cross-training can be a tough concept for those who don't believe that workout variety is the spice of training life. It's more than just trying to find the extra time – after all, a 30-minute run is often difficult enough to fit in. So where are you going to find the time to swim, cycle, lift weights and all the rest?

Maybe we feel under pressure to put more effort into cross-training because of the increasing interest in triathlons and other multi-discipline events. To be an elite triathlete, some people will spend many hours a day training. Who needs all of it?

Fortunately, no one but an elite athlete. Still, the rest of us can benefit from more realistic doses of cross-training. However, it's hard to work out where to begin, how much and what kinds of cross-training to do.

Life used to be simple. Runners ran and swimmers swam. Cyclists pedalled and weight-lifters grunted. Then everything got mixed up. Runners started cycling, swimmers lifted weights and cyclists started running. Now, it's not unusual to see athletes climbing stairs that go nowhere, or cross-country skiing over a gym floor or doing that weird circular running thing with the poles. These activities may well look odd but they're very good for you. You'll stretch certain muscles, strengthen others and burn plenty of calories.

Which is all well and good but what exactly can cross-training do for runners? And, given all the cross-training choices, which disciplines are the best ones for you?

THE DO MORE, GET FITTER THEORY
Proponents of this position believe that runners should cross-train with exercises and activities that are as close to running as possible.
THE LOGIC The stronger you make the muscles you use for running, the better you'll run.

THE REST THEORY
According to this approach, runners should cross-train with sports that are as different from running as possible.
THE LOGIC You can burn calories and get a good workout, and, at the same time, you'll be resting your running muscles and won't be creating the one-sport muscle imbalances that often can lead to an unfortunate injury.

THE SPECIFICITY THEORY
Specificity advocates believe that runners shouldn't cross-train – and that's the end of it. It's a waste of time and will only tire you for your next run. When you need a day off from running, take a day off from everything.
THE LOGIC All training should be specific to the sport it is aimed towards, so therefore the best way to train for running is to run.

No wonder so many runners are confused. Who are they supposed to believe, and which theory should they follow? 'All of the approaches make sense and could work,' says Dr Mike Flynn, an exercise physiologist and one of America's leading researchers in the field of cross-training. The trick to optimising your training programme, he explains, is to pick the approach that best fits your current training goals in both running and fitness. To make your decision easier, we've designed these cross-training programmes for five different types of runner. Simply choose the category that describes you the best over the page and follow the suggested advice. It's time to get cross. ▶

BEGINNER

This is for runners who do 5-15 miles per week.

THE BASICS If you're running to get into shape, the first thing you need to do is build up your cardiovascular system. A strong heart and lungs will supply more fuel to your working leg muscles and allow you to run without constantly feeling as if you are out of breath.

If you're switching to running from another sport, you're probably fit enough to run a few miles without much problem, but don't overdo it. Running involves more pounding than most other sports, and it takes time for the muscles, tendons and ligaments to adapt.

THE PROGRAMME The best cross-training programme for beginners is one that mixes running and cross-training in equal amounts. If you're running twice a week, try cross-training twice a week as well. This will allow you to build your cardio system and muscle strength without undue risk of injury. If you can't handle more than one hard run a week, split your workouts between running and cross-training.

THE EXERCISES As a beginner, almost any aerobic activity will help to increase your cardiovascular strength. The best exercises are those that also strengthen as many of your running muscles as possible. These exercises will improve the co-ordination of your running muscles and teach them to process and store fuel more effectively.

INTERMEDIATE

This is for runners who do 15-40 miles per week.

THE BASICS You have developed a strong cardio system through your running so easy cross-training workouts won't improve your running performance. You need to choose cross-training activities that either provide a very high-intensity cardiovascular workout or specifically target your running muscles.

THE PROGRAMME Run two to three times as much as you are cross-training. Run for two or three days, and then do cross-training. If you are doing two hard runs a week, select cross-training workouts that allow you to exercise at a moderate pace. You should be using these workouts just to give your running muscles some extra training without extra pounding. If your body can really handle only one hard run a week, then one of your cross-training workouts should be hard also.

THE EXERCISES Cross-training exercises that provide high-intensity cardio workouts are cross-country skiing, stair climbing and high-cadence stationary cycling. Grinding away in a high gear on a bike will slow your turnover, but using a high cadence (over 90rpm) will keep you quick and allow you to get your heart rate up.

ADVANCED

This is for those who run more than 40 miles per week.

THE BASICS You have probably maximised your cardiovascular conditioning, as well as the strength of your leg muscles, so cross-training won't directly do you much good. To improve your running performance, you need more quality in your runs. Running coaches and exercise physiologists generally recommend at least two hard runs a week – a shorter interval session on the track and a longer tempo run.

SWIM TO WIN
Make a splash with
your training routine

THE PROGRAMME Since both hard running and high mileage can increase your injury risk, your best bet may be complete rest rather than cross-training. This will allow your muscles to recover completely for your next run. If you don't want to take days off, you can consider low-intensity cross-training with a sport that doesn't tax your running muscles. This will

> A STRONG HEART
> AND LUNGS WILL
> SUPPLY MORE
> FUEL TO YOUR
> LEG MUSCLES

if you're unsure, ask your doctor. And to reduce the risk, don't do more than a single high-intensity workout per week.

THE EXERCISES So, injury-prone runners should keep their cross-training workouts as specific to training as possible. In-line skating, stair climbing, rowing and cross-country skiing are good choices. Unfortunately, some injuries – stress fractures in particular – don't allow many cross-training options. In these cases, cross-training in the pool by swimming or deep-water running is the best alternative. These are non-weight-bearing activities that don't hurt the legs.

INURY-PRONE

This is for runners who experience two or more running injuries in any given year.

THE BASICS Surveys show two out of three runners will be injured in the course of a year. Cross-training can help in two ways. Firstly, it can keep you healthy by allowing you to stay fit without the constant pounding of running. Secondly, cross-training can help forestall the performance losses that come when an injury keeps you from running. Studies have shown that runners can maintain their running times for up to six weeks by cross-training alone if it is done at the proper intensity.

THE PROGRAMME The best cross-training programme for injury-prone runners involves doing two to four runs per week (depending on how much your body can tolerate) and two cross-training workouts. Both of your cross-training workouts should target running-specific muscles in order to help to increase their strength and efficiency without subjecting them to more pavement pounding.
The extra training of these muscles through cross-training rarely produces injuries because high impact is the main injury cause, but

GENERAL

This is for low- to mid-mileage runners more concerned with overall fitness than racing.

THE BASICS Look at any elite runner, and you'll notice that running doesn't do much for the upper body. It also neglects quadriceps in favour of the calves, hamstrings and buttocks. Furthermore, after the age of 30, all the muscles in our bodies begin to lose strength. Fortunately, exercise can cut the rate almost in half.

THE PROGRAMME For total-body fitness, run twice a week and do a complementary exercise on one or two other days of the week. In addition, 20 minutes of circuit weight training twice a week will help you condition all of those muscles that may have been missed out.

THE EXERCISES General-fitness runners need exercises that target the upper body and quads. Try rowing, swimming or using an elliptical trainer to ensure you work your upper body, too. ∎

burn calories, and variety will keep you mentally fresh.
If you choose to cross-train, replace one or two of your easy runs – the ones that come a day after a hard run – with a cross-training activity.

THE EXERCISES Cycling, pool running, swimming and rowing give your running muscles a break and let them recover for your next hard run.

Photography **Getty**

WEIGHTS GAIN
Strength training
doesn't mean a weak
performance

RUNNING
STRONG

Myths about strength training can prevent runners from working to their full potential

Often I hear false or misguided notions about weight training,' says Luke Carlson, coach of both elite athletes and competitive recreational runners. 'Certainly, running should always be the primary focus of your training programme. However, strength training presents a different physiological stimulus, one that includes a host of distinct benefits that running doesn't provide, but which are crucial to health and optimal performance.' Here is a primer to help you safely become a stronger runner.

MYTH 1

Runners don't need to lift weights. If they want to get stronger, they should run more.

TRUTH

Strength training works in two ways: it prevents injuries and enhances performance. Properly carried out, strength training provides the foundation for injury-free running and the ability to adhere to a regime of mileage, speed and tempo work. Numerous studies have proven that strength training will enhance running performance. A 2013 review of research in the Scandinavian *Journal of Medicine and Science in Sports* showed that resistance training improves running economy and builds muscle fibres. Other studies have linked weight training to better body composition and resting metabolic rates. As we age, strength training is particularly important – studies have shown that running does not offer protection against the gradual loss of lean muscle tissue. And as we lose muscle, we also lose a larger percentage of our fast-twitch muscle fibres. ▶

MYTH 2

Body-weight exercises are better for runners than going to the weights room.

TRUTH

A strength-training exercise is simply a biomechanical or anatomical movement with resistance. The resistance may come from a band, machine, free weight or your body weight – our muscles can't decipher where the resistance originates. So a lunge, a squat and a leg press are in some ways the same exercise – they involve knee extension and hip extension caused by the contraction of the glutes and quadriceps. Over the years, we have come to look at certain exercises as more fundamental, but there is really no scientific or theoretical basis for this. For example, some say beginners shouldn't bench press; they should do press-ups instead. But a press-up represents far too much resistance for some people. A bench press (or any type of machine that involves a press) allows for many different resistance increments, so it can be better for beginners.

MYTH 3

Working the core is key as running trains all other areas.

TRUTH

Research indicates that upper-body, lower-body and midsection strength training all contribute to improved running performance. You should do exercises that involve all the major muscle groups. Rather than strengthening an area you assume is weak, you are better off developing strength in all muscle groups, which will create balance and synergy.

MYTH 5

You need to do plenty of reps if you want to build any endurance strength for distance running.

TRUTH

The number of repetitions is not critically important. Runners have been told to perform a high number of reps to specifically enhance muscle endurance. Research has revealed that doing five reps or 20 reps will produce the same benefit in terms of muscle strength and endurance. Just make sure that they're good-quality reps – that is to say they're unhurried and you go through the full range of movement.

MYTH 4

You need to strength train several times a week to see benefits.

TRUTH

A very small amount of strength training can bring tremendous benefit to a runner. More is not better – strength train only once or twice per week. Your total weekly strength-training time commitment should be 30-60 minutes.

MYTH 6

Use light weights and don't exhaust yourself.

TRUTH

Many runners assume that lifting heavy weights is a good way to get injured. In fact, fast movements that create high external forces on joints are more likely to set you up for injury. Lift a weight heavy enough to exhaust you in eight to 20 reps. Train to the point of momentary muscle fatigue. Focus on continuing each set of exercises until it is impossible to complete another perfect rep. This ensures optimal muscle fibre involvement.

MUSCLE UP
The stronger
you are the
faster you go

SAMPLE WORKOUTS

Key moves to boost injury prevention and performance

Try the following two strength-training workouts, once or twice a week. Use weights, machines and body weight. They promote injury prevention, improve body composition and performance.

WORKOUT 1
LEGS
- Leg press, squat or lunge
- Leg curl
- Leg extension
- Ankle dorsiflexion
- Single-leg hip flexion

UPPER BODY
- Shoulder press
- Pulldown
- Chest press

MIDSECTION
- Crunch
- Low-back extension

WORKOUT 2
LEGS
- Leg press, squat or lunge
- Hip adductor
- Hip abductor
- Calf/heel raise

UPPER BODY
- Incline press
- Seated row
- Dip/press-up
- Shoulder shrug
- Lateral raise

MIDSECTION
- Torso rotation

MYTH 7

Lift with quick movements for more power and speed.

TRUTH

Lift and lower the weight slowly. Take two to three seconds to lift the weight and at least four seconds to lower it. A mantra for the runner is, 'To become fast, lift slowly.' If you move quickly, you incorporate momentum, unload your muscles and minimise muscle fibre involvement.

Also, the faster you move, the greater the forces on your joints and connective tissue, and the greater the risk for injury. To create explosive effort without the risks, plan to lift the weight as fast as you possibly can near the end of each set of exercises, when you are fatigued. Fast movement will be impossible, but you'll still recruit fast-twitch fibres.

CENTRE OF
ATTENTION

Forget crunches: if you want to get faster, fitter and stronger, you need to train your core like a runner

n the past you'd have been hard-pressed to find elite runners paying attention to their abdominal muscles. Today, it's almost mandatory. 'It's so important. The stronger the core, the more likely you are to hold your form and less likely to get injured,' explains marathon world record holder Paula Radcliffe. You simply can't run your personal best without a strong core: the muscles in your abdominals, lower back and glutes. They provide the stability, power and endurance that runners need for powering up hills, sprinting to the finish and maintaining form mile after mile.

'When your core is strong, everything else will follow,' says running coach Greg McMillan, who has worked with scores of elite and recreational runners. 'It's the foundation for all of your movement, no matter what level of running you're doing.'

The key is to train your core like a specialist would. Quality core work is by no means easy, but it doesn't require that much of your time, says running coach Nick Anderson. 'You don't need to put in any more than 15 minutes just a few times a week.' It's an investment that will pay dividends when you are out on the road. ➢

KNOW YOUR **CORE**

A close look at the muscle groups that make up your core

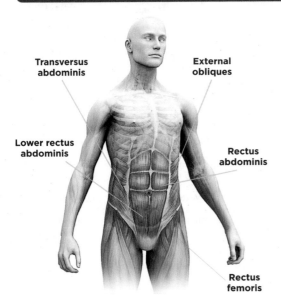

Transversus abdominis

External obliques

Lower rectus abdominis

Rectus abdominis

Rectus femoris

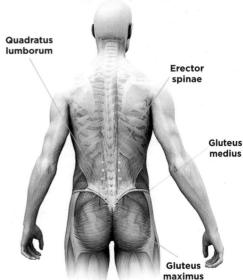

Quadratus lumborum

Erector spinae

Gluteus medius

Gluteus maximus

Photography **Sarah A Friedman** Illustrations **Supercorn, John McNeil**

HARD CORE
Put your best
foot forward with
these key moves

CORE **VALUES**

Here's how a strong midsection will help avoid injury and finish races faster

SPEED

As you extend your stride or quicken the rate of your leg and foot turnover when you're trying to pick up the pace, the lower abs and lower back are called into action. The stronger and more stable these muscles are, the more force you can generate as you push off the ground.

UPHILLS

If your core is strong, your legs will have a stable plane to push from, for a more powerful ascent. When you swing your leg forward, the hip-flexor muscles, such as the rectus femoris, pull on the pelvis. As you push off the ground, the glutes and hamstrings are engaged.

DOWNHILLS

You need strong gluteal muscles to help absorb the impact and counter the momentum of the forward motion. Without core strength, your quads and knee joints bear the extra pounding of your body weight, which can lead to fatigue, pain and serious injury.

ENDURANCE

As you near the end of a race, a solid core helps you maintain proper form and run efficiently, even through fatigue. With strong lower abs and lower-back muscles, it's easier to stay upright. A weak core can put too much stress on your hips, knees and shins.

LATERAL MOVEMENT

Whenever you have to suddenly move to the side the obliques provide stability and help keep you upright. If your core is weak, then you may end up leaning into the movement, which can put excess weight and strain on the joints in your legs and feet.

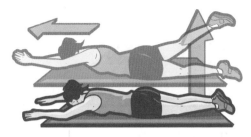

SUPERMAN

WHAT IT HITS Transversus abdominis (deep abdominals) and erector spinae (lower back).

HOW Start face down on the floor, with your arms and legs extended out in front. Raise your head, your left arm, and right leg five inches off the floor. Hold for three counts, then lower. Repeat with your right arm and left leg. Do up to 10 reps each side.

GET IT RIGHT Don't raise your shoulders too much.

MAKE IT HARDER Lift both arms and legs off the ground at the same time.

BEYOND CRUNCHES

A 15-minute workout for runners

Fortunately, quality core strength work doesn't require a great deal of time or equipment – just 15 minutes three times a week, a few feet of floor space and some key moves done correctly and consistently. This workout is designed by Greg McMillan, a running coach and exercise scientist, who has worked with recreational runners and world-class athletes. The workout is devised to strengthen specific muscles runners need for bounding up hills, sprinting to the finish, enduring long distances and preventing running injuries. Try doing two sets of these moves right before or after your run, three times a week.

BRIDGE

WHAT IT HITS Glutes and hamstrings.

HOW Lie face up on the floor, with your knees bent 90 degrees, your feet on the floor. Lift your hips and back off the floor until your body forms a line from your shoulders to your knees. Hold for five to 10 seconds. Lower and repeat 10 to 12 times.

GET IT RIGHT Squeeze your glutes at the top of the movement and don't let your spine sag.

MAKE IT HARDER Straighten one leg and point it out while your hips are up.

METRONOME

WHAT IT HITS Obliques.

HOW Lie face up with your knees bent and raised over your hips, your feet lifted, and your arms out. Rotate your legs to the left, bringing your knees as close to the floor as possible without touching. Return to the centre, then rotate your knees to the right. Do 10 to 12 reps on each side.

GET IT RIGHT Don't swing your hips or use momentum

MAKE IT HARDER Keep your legs straight. ›

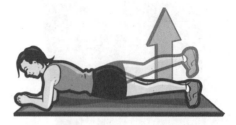

SIDE PLANK

WHAT IT HITS Obliques, transversus abdominis, lower back, hips and glutes.

HOW Lie on your right side, supporting your upper body on your right forearm, with your left arm at your side. Lift your hips and, keeping your body weight supported on the forearm and the side of the right foot, extend your left arm above your shoulder. Hold for 10-30 seconds. Switch sides and then repeat.

GET IT RIGHT Maintain a straight line from ankle to shoulder. Keep your hips up; don't let them sag.

MAKE IT HARDER Support your upper body with your right hand, not your forearm.

PLANK LIFT

WHAT IT HITS Transversus abdominis and lower back.

HOW Begin face down on the floor, propped up on your forearms, with knees and feet together. With your elbows under your shoulders, lift your torso, legs and hips in a straight line. Hold for 10 seconds. Raise your right leg a few inches, keeping the rest of the body still. Lower and repeat with your left leg.

GET IT RIGHT Pull in your belly and don't let your hips sag down towards the floor.

MAKE IT HARDER Extend the time of the exercise each time it becomes too easy.

ALL THE RIGHT **MOVES**

A few quick fixes to your training will pay off on the run

THE MISTAKE
You're doing the wrong exercises
'The biggest mistake that runners tend to make is to take strength-training moves, such as crunches, straight from the fitness industry,' says running coach Greg McMillan. For most runners, standard crunches aren't helpful because they don't work the deep core muscles that provide the stability to run mile after mile.
THE FIX
Do workouts that hit the muscles and movements that runners need. Exercises like the side plank or plank lift strengthen the obliques, on the sides of the trunk, and the transverse abs; these core muscles wrap around your trunk like a corset.

THE MISTAKE
You're a creature of habit
Even if you've moved beyond crunches, you may find you have slipped into a non-beneficial routine. 'You need to constantly challenge your muscles to get the best results,' says running coach Sam Murphy.
THE FIX
You need to mix up your training. Fine-tune your workout to make it more difficult than your previous sessions. Try balancing on one leg or changing your arm position. At the gym, use devices like a stability ball – an unstable platform that forces your core muscles to work harder to keep you steady. And as a rule, McMillan says, you should try to change your routine around every six weeks or so.

THE MISTAKE
You whip through your workouts
If you're flying through the moves in your workout, you're using momentum, not muscles.
THE FIX
Slow it down. Exercises like the plank, which require holding one position for 10-60 seconds, force you to work your muscles continuously. Even in exercises that involve repetitions, make steady – not rapid-fire – movements. 'It takes intention,' says Paula Coates, running coach, physiotherapist and author of *Running Repairs: A Runner's Guide to Keeping Injury Free* (A&C Black Publishers Ltd). 'You must not rush your exercises or you can't be sure you're doing them properly.'

THE MISTAKE
You ignore what you don't see
Runners often have weak backs because they just forget about them, out of sight, out of mind, says running coach Nick Anderson. 'But when you're running, especially if you're running for a long time, those muscles in the lower back are crucial for providing you with much-needed stability and good support.'
THE FIX
Include at least one – but ideally more than one – exercise that targets the lower back area and glutes in each workout. Moves like the bridge and superman (previous page), help build muscles that will support and protect the spine, maintaining a healthy back.

CRUNCH TIME
You can do it if
you put your
back into it

CORE
MELTDOWN
Maintain it correctly or
suffer the consequences

Your core is like a power plant. If it's not working efficiently, you'll waste energy, says Tim Hilden, a physical therapist, coach and physiologist who specialises in running. 'You'll see too much unwanted movement, which decreases performance or sets you up for injury.' Here are three areas that can be injured as a result of a weak core.

LOWER BACK
As your legs pound the pavement, your vertebrae absorb much of the force. That shock worsens if your core is weak, which will produce lower-back pain. Build those muscles with moves like the superman (page 69).

HAMSTRINGS
When your core isn't stable, your hamstrings often have to work extra hard, says running coach and physiotherapist Paula Coates. The added work can leave them shorter, tighter and more vulnerable to injury. To strengthen them, as well as your glutes, try exercises like bridges, lunges and squats.

KNEES
Without a stable core, you can't control the movement of your torso as well, and you risk putting excess force on your joints each time your foot lands. This can lead to pain under the knee (known as 'runner's knee'), patellar tendinitis (a sharp pain in the bottom of the knee), and iliotibial-band syndrome. The planks (opposite) strengthens the transversus abdominis, which help steady the core and prevent injury. ■

MASTERS OF *TIME*

Want to get fitter and healthier as you get older?
Follow these guidelines for runners over 40

Masters athletes are proving that as much as 70 per cent of age-related decline is due not to ageing but to deconditioning – losing physical fitness by doing very little. Scientists who've studied endurance athletes have discovered 80-year-olds with muscles and cardiac capacities akin to those of 20-year-olds. And elite women masters (over 40) runners, especially, are turning in performances that are forcing us to redefine how long our so-called athletic prime can last.

For example, the marathon world record in the 50-plus age group is 2:31:05, set in 2005 by Ukrainian Tatyana Pozdniakova. That time would have put her in the top half of finishers in the London 2012 Olympics. 'We're just learning what the human body is capable of,' says Greg Wells, author of *Superbodies: Peak Performance Secrets from the World's Best Athletes* (Harper Collins) and a professor of physiology and health at the University of Toronto, Canada. 'We have to throw out all our preconceived notions about ageing,' he says.

Wells believes that exercise is the most powerful tool we have to forestall ageing and possibly prevent – or even help treat – just about every chronic disease that exists today. 'If we had a drug that did what exercise did, it would be the biggest revolution ever and would be promoted all over the world. And all you have to do is go out for a run,' he says.

'A lot of research now shows that training has effects on the human body at any age,' says Wells. 'Exercise can help keep you young.' Our bodies will still age, of course, that's unfortunately unavoidable. But runners who stick with the programme can delay the decline. We may have to work for it, but it's worth it.

1

TIME WILL TELL
INJURY RISK
In a study of 2,500 older athletes by Dr Vonda Wright, orthopaedic surgeon and author of *Fitness after 40* (Amacom), 89 per cent of subjects had experienced at least one sports-related injury since turning 50.

DECLINING CARDIAC OUTPUT
On average, the amount of oxygen we can take in and pump to our muscles declines at a rate of about one per cent a year between the ages of 35 and 70.

SLOWING TIMES
Performance typically drops off by about one per cent a year between the ages of 30 and 50, by two per cent between 50 and 75, then by six to eight per cent a year thereafter.

LOSS OF LUNG CAPACITY
Your maximum breathing capacity can decline by up to 40 per cent between the ages of 20 and 70.

LOSS OF DEXTERITY AND FLEXIBILITY
Muscles, ligaments and tendons all become stiffer with age. Flexibility can decline by six per cent in every decade after the age of 50, even if you're exercising regularly.

LOSS OF BONE DENSITY
After the age of 30, the quantity of bone cells can decline at a rate of 0.3 to two per cent a year. For women, menopause can accelerate the loss to over three per cent in the two to three years beforehand and for up to 10 years afterwards.

LOSS OF MUSCLE MASS
Between the ages of 50 and 70 it's possible to lose about 15 per cent of our lean muscle ⟩

mass each decade. Time doesn't stem the flow either: after 70, it's 30 per cent.

LOSS OF OESTROGEN
This powerful steroid hormone reduces inflammation, stimulates muscle repair and regeneration, and enables women to burn fat. Post-menopausal women have about the same amount of the hormone as men do.

2
TRAIN IN THREE ZONES
ZONE 1
EASY RUNNING
75 per cent of weekly mileage
Masters runners should spend the vast majority of their training time in this easy zone, says Jason Vescovi, an exercise physiologist. It gently stresses the body into making myriad adaptations. Tendons and muscles (including the heart) become stronger, as do the lungs; the number of red blood cells increases; blood vessels develop ever more capillaries; and mitochondria, those microscopic, power-generating parts of cells that convert food into fuel, both multiply and become up to 35 per cent larger, so they can burn even more fat and produce even more energy.

ZONE 2
TARGET RACE PACES
Five to 10 per cent of weekly mileage
This second training zone is often called the tempo zone. (Use a GPS to set and monitor your pace, or try the talk test – you shouldn't be able to complete full sentences.) Although it corresponds to race paces, Vescovi recommends spending the least amount of time running in this zone – five to 10 per cent, or one run a week. That's because most adaptations occur in that first (aerobic) and in the third zones.

ZONE 3
FAST RUNNING OR HILLS
15-20 per cent weekly mileage
This toughest training zone is sometimes called the anaerobic or lactate-threshold zone. The intense training delivers massive rewards, boosting VO_2 max, increasing your body's ability to convert lactic acid to fuel and improving overall cardiovascular capacity. This kind of tough training also injects your body with youthful vitality by stressing it just enough to make it release human growth hormone, which rushes in to repair, rebuild and renew muscles. Working at this intensity will also help restore your youthful figure, as it brings on an intense calorie burn.

3
MORE IS BETTER
As for what dose a runner needs in order to stay fit into old age Wells says that more exercise is almost always better than less. 'I believe training for a marathon is good for your health,' he says, 'because it stresses the oxygen-transport pathway; it puts pressure on your lungs, heart, blood, muscles, brain and nervous system. The stress stimulates your body to adapt and improve, and it will continue to do so as long as it also has time to recover.'

Scientific dogma used to say when we reached 60 our bodies lost the ability to adapt to exercise. Now research and the stunning performances of masters athletes show older people can adapt with the same relative improvements as young adults – in bone density, aerobic capacity, muscle strength and general cardiovascular fitness.

Excerpted from Older, Faster, Stronger: What Women Runners Can Teach Us All About Living Younger, Longer, by Margaret Webb (Rodale). Available from Amazon.co.uk

10:00

You can see the benefit from just 10 minutes of strength work a day.

Cut 10 minutes from your run a few times a week and perform the following moves. The workout is designed by Cathy Utzschneider, champion masters runner, coach and author of *Mastering Running* (Human Kinetics).

0 1:00
SIDE PLANK

30 seconds on each side

IN THE LONG RUN

Olympic medallist Deena Kastor's fastest days may be behind her but she still thrives on racing goals

America's Deena Kastor was a bronze medallist in the 2004 Athens Olympic Marathon. Now, at an age when many elites retire – Kastor turned 42 in 2015 – she is still making headlines.

In September 2014 she broke the women's masters half-marathon world record, clocking 1:09:36 in the Rock 'n' Roll Philadelphia Half. In the process, she also set three more masters records for 15K (49:03), 10 miles (52:41) and 20K (1:05:52).

But Kastor isn't racing just for titles or records. With her elite days behind her and the new demands of work and family in front of her, chasing a record is simply a way to keep pulling the best out of herself. Because, as Kastor has learned, age doesn't dampen one's competitive spirit – or love for the sport.

These days, she runs about half the miles she used to as an elite athlete. It's easy to assume that the transition to a second – slower – phase of her career would be difficult. But Kastor has embraced it. 'It's since turning 40 that I have truly seen the value in running, racing and pushing my own limits,' she says.

She thrives on training, racing and chasing a goal. 'A goal is an awesome way to force growth on yourself,' she says.

Her fastest times are in the past, so Kastor focuses on the present. 'I'm not comparing myself to the runner from 2006 [when she set her half and marathon PBs],' she says. 'I'm comparing myself to last week or maybe two weeks ago. I can say, "Wow, I just ran five seconds faster," for example.'

There is, at least, one certainty for Kastor: 'I may not be travelling the world and competing, but I'll still be running repeats when I'm 60.' ■

IN YOUR OWN *TIME*

03:00 LUNGE — 1 minute leading with each leg

05:00 FRONT PLANK

07:00 STRAIGHT-LEG DONKEY KICK — 30 seconds per leg

09:00 SQUAT

04:00 SEATED RUNNING ARMS

06:00 BENT-LEG DONKEY KICK — 30 seconds per leg

08:00 PRESS-UP

10:00 DIP WITH A BENCH OR CHAIR

Photography **Johanna Parkin** Styling **Maud Eden**

CHAPTER | **3**

RUNNING
NUTRITION

Find all the advice you need on healthy eating
plans that will help you on the road to victory

FEED YOUR *GOAL*

Make sure your weekly shopping list reflects the aims of your training regime

HOW TO USE THESE PAGES

1 Firstly use the category headings to help you to identify the body benefits that you're after.

2 Narrow it down by selecting the various foods from within that category that best suit your needs.

3 Add the selected foods together to assemble your weekly shopping list, knowing that you'll be supplying your body with potent and plentiful sources of the nutrients needed to compliment and improve your running.

PREVENT INURY

RED PEPPER
Has 300 per cent of your daily vitamin C requirement, more than any citrus fruit. Vit C is crucial for repairing connective tissue and staving off colds.
Per week: 3 peppers

EDAMAME
These beans contain soy protein, which is rich in anti-inflammatory isoflavonoids. Oklahoma State University, found eating it daily for three months lessened knee pain.
Per week: 100g x3

OLIVE OIL MARGARINE
A great source of bone-building vitamin D, says sports dietitian Karen Reid – especially important as research shows more than three-quarters of all adults are D-deficient.
Per week: on toast x3

BLUEBERRIES
Packed with vitamin C, vitamin K and manganese, these berries help to improve bone strength, according to research in the *Journal of Bone and Mineral Research*.
Per week: handful x3

HONEY
The amino acids in the sticky sweet stuff help your body absorb bone-boosting calcium effectively, say scientists at Purdue University, US.
Per week: 1 tbsp x3

PUMPKIN SEEDS
These are packed full of magnesium, which fights the ageing of the cells that create collagen in your tendons and ligaments, found research in the *Proceedings of the National Academies of Sciences*.
Per week: 20g x3

SMOKED MACKEREL
The fish's omega-3 fatty acids significantly reduce joint pain and shorten the duration of morning joint stiffness – so say researchers at Harvard Medical School in the US.
Per week: fillet x2

Photography Getty, Studio 33

RUN FURTHER

CHAMPAGNE
Raise a glass to your heart, say Reading University scientists. Their studies found the polyphenols in bubbly reduce the loss of nitric oxide from the blood, improving circulation.
Per week: 3 glasses

MARMITE
Try to love it for your heart's sake: Bristol University found its benfotiamine has a beneficial effect on your cardiovascular function.
Per week: on toast x3

TOFU
Bean curd is a source of unsaturated fats. A study in the *Journal of the American College of Cardiology* found eating these fats post-exercise boosts blood flow by 45 per cent.
Per week: 150g x2

STEAK
Each footstrike damages red blood cells, lowering your levels of iron – key to getting oxygen to the working muscles. The iron in steak is easily absorbed, says Reid.
Per week: 150g fillet x2

APPLE
It's crunch time. The quercetin found in apples improves lung capacity and protects against pollution, say scientists at the St George's Hospital, London.

AVOCADO
The sodium, potassium and magnesium in these improve lung volume and oxygen flow, says a study in the *American Journal of Epidemiology*.
Per week: 2 ▶

EAT ON THE GO
The tastier way to becoming a better runner

FASTER FOODS
Chuck them in your
basket (try not to
make a mess)

A PRE-RUN CHOCOLATE MILK BOOSTS MUSCLE REPAIR FOR THREE HOURS

MAINTAIN MUSCLE

CHOCOLATE MILK
Drinking fat-free chocolate milk before a run promotes muscle repair for up to three hours afterwards, according to the University of Connecticut US.
Per week: 330ml x2

SPINACH
The nitric oxide reduces the oxygen needed to power muscles by five per cent, according to the Karolinska Institute in Sweden.
Per week: 300g x2

EGGS
Egg protein is the most balanced food protein after human breast milk, which means it contains all the crucial amino acids your muscles need for recovery. One egg will deliver 10 per cent of your daily protein needs.
Per week: 3

PORK FILLET
A tasty way to get lean, mean, high-quality protein. It also contains thiamine, which is key to efficient metabolism of carbohydrate into energy, and to the repair of your muscle fibres.
Per week: 150g x2

POMEGRANATE JUICE
Ellagitannin, a phytonutrient found in pomegranates, reduces inflammation and post-workout soreness, according to research by physiologists at the University of Texas, US.
Per week: 200ml x3

SWEET POTATO
It has a low Glycaemic Index (GI) rating which means it gives you a slow, sustained energy release. It also has trace minerals manganese and copper – both crucial for healthy muscle function.
Per week: 3

ALMONDS
These tasty nuts are one of the best sources of alpha-tocopherol vitamin E. This can help prevent damage being done by free radicals as a result of the oxidisation in your muscles after hard efforts.
Per week: handful x7

GET LEAN

GREEN TEA
EGCG – a compound found in most green teas – speeds up your metabolism so that you burn more calories. Jasmine tea has the same properties, too.
Per week: 4 cups

CHILLIES
The capsaicin in chilli peppers can help manage appetite and burn more calories after your meal, say researchers at Purdue University in the US.
Per week: ½ tsp x3

LAMB
Don't shy away from a Sunday roast. Lamb packs carnitine – a mix of amino acids that shuttles fat into the mitochondria (the cells' power producers), where it's metabolised.
Per week: 150g x2

PINE NUTS
Korean researchers found eating pine kernels prompts your body to release cholecystokinin – a hormone that suppresses your appetite.
Per week: 3x 20g

GRAPEFRUIT
Research at Scripps Clinic, San Diego, US, found eating grapefruit before meals helped dieters lose up to 4.5kg in 12 weeks. A compound in the fruit lowers insulin, controlling hunger.
Per week: half x9

COCONUT OIL
A study in the *Journal of Nutrition* found eating this regularly resulted in a rise in metabolism and a higher rate of calorie-burning.
Per week: 1 tbsp x3

RUN FASTER

COFFEE
Caffeine before an eight-miler improves times by 24 seconds or more, says the *Journal of Sports Science*.
Per week: 6 cups

WATERMELON
Citrulline in this fruit buffers muscle fatigue, so you can push harder, says a study the University of Córdoba, Spain.
Per week: 300g x3

BEETROOT
St Louis University, US, found you can run five per cent faster after eating beetroot. Its nitrates boost blood flow.
Per week: 3

BRAN FLAKES
Betaine in bran helps with hydration, found The College of New Jersey, US. So you can train harder, for longer.
Per week: 30g x3

STAY HEALTHY

MUSHROOMS
The humble button protects your immune system, say researchers at Arizona State University, US.
Per week: 100g x3

KALE
The prebiotics in this green are a type of beneficial fibre that helps feed 'good' probiotic gut bacteria.
Per week: 150g x2

CAPERS
US scientists from Appalachian State University found daily doses of quercetin, present in capers, reduced viral infections.
Per week: handful x2

WALNUTS
Omega-3s in walnuts help reduce cholesterol, found a study in the *Journal of the American College of Nutrition*.
Per week: handful x3

FATS &
FIGURES

New research suggests saturated fat may not be a no-no after all. So should we be rethinking the butter and burgers?

For decades, nutrition rules have put strict limits on saturated fat. Even as far back as the 1960s, experts were pretty unanimous in decreeing that eating foods high in saturated fats, such as red meat and full-fat dairy, increased your risk of heart disease. And people concerned with the health and function of their bodies took heed, severely curtailing their intake of such foods.

However, several recent headline-grabbing studies have challenged this age-old nutritional commandment. One

were not designed to find direct cause and effect. They also relied on participants to self-report their diets, and with the best will in the world, such accounts are often inaccurate.

But through randomised, controlled clinical studies, researchers do know some things for certain. 'Saturated fat raises LDL cholesterol levels,' says Penny Kris-Etherton, professor of nutrition at Penn State University, US. Because LDL can contribute to plaque deposits in arteries, 'it is one of the two major risk factors for cardiovascular disease', she

to be immediately burned for energy rather than stored. It's also emerged taking saturated fat out of our diets has a strange effect: it lowers levels of 'good' HDL cholesterol, which clears bad LDL from the bloodstream.

'All foods fit into a healthy diet,' says sports nutritionist Heather Fink. 'Runners are active and health conscious, and often restrict those foods. when they don't have to.'

Making the right choice involves looking at the total food versus a single nutrient. Some foods higher in saturated fat are really nutritious – and excluding them means you miss out. For example, red meat contains iron, zinc and protein; whole milk is an excellent source of bone-building calcium and vitamin D; and grass-fed beef and dairy provide conjugated linoleic acids, which have been linked to weight loss. Plus, full-fat foods are more flavorful and satisfying, which can reduce appetite, says Volek.

RESEARCH HAS DISCOVERED THAT SATURATED FAT MAY HAVE HEALTH BENEFITS

of those, published in the *Annals of Internal Medicine* early last year, reviewed 76 studies and found no association between saturated fat and heart disease. Another review, published in 2010, reached a similar conclusion. 'Saturated fat may not be the demon it was made out to be,' says Jeff Volek, a professor of kinesiology at the University of Connecticut, US, and a dietitian.

Before you celebrate this news with a bacon double cheeseburger, there's a catch: just because these study reviews didn't find an association doesn't mean there isn't one. Many of these studies

says. Kris-Etherton adds that when 'good' polyunsaturated fats (found in fish and vegetable oils) are substituted for saturated fat, LDL levels go down and so does the incidence of heart disease. And there are other reasons to err on the side of caution: diets high in saturated fat have been linked to some cancers, and processed meats to increased diabetes risk.

But it's not all bad news. Research has discovered that saturated fat may have health benefits. For example, certain medium-chain saturated fats, such as lauric acid (found in coconut oil), have the potential

A varied diet of natural whole foods – including some saturated fat – can supply a range of nutrients that keep you in top running form. So enjoy that chicken with the skin on (once in a while) and spread butter on your toast (occasionally). As long as you're also eating plenty of vegetables, fruits, wholegrains and lean protein, you'll be doing your body – and your running – a lot of good.

HOLIER THAN COW
The blessed burger
could now be back on
the healthy menu

SAT-FAT SUPERSTARS

CHICKEN THIGHS
High in zinc,
which boosts the
immune system.
3g sat fat per 100g

EGGS
Packed with
protein and
essential
amino acids.
2g sat fat per egg

CHEDDAR CHEESE
One fifth of your
daily calcium
needs per slice.
21g sat fat per 100g

MACADAMIA NUTS
Packed with the
essential mineral
manganese.
10g sat fat per 100g

FULL-FAT YOGHURT
Lots of probiotics,
which are linked
to weight loss.
2g sat fat per 100g

RED MEAT
A good source of
energy-supplying
vitamin B12.
3g sat fat per 100g

FANCY SOME BUTTER IN YOUR *COFFEE?*

Some elite runners are starting to make their coffee 'bullet-proof'. But is this really a good idea?

There's a trend among some runners for blending butter and oil (such as coconut) into coffee – a drink called 'bulletproof coffee', after Dave Asprey's book, The Bulletproof Diet (£12.91, Rodale). Fans claim it provides lasting energy, staves off hunger and helps burn fat. 'It's a super-creamy, frothy, delicious coffee that will blow your mind and give you hours of long-lasting energy,' says US two-time Olympic marathoner Ryan Hall. 'The fat helps keep my hormones at the right levels.' Some of the claims stand up, says sports nutritionist Liz Applegate. 'This drink can contain over 400 calories and at least 200mg of caffeine, so it's no surprise you feel good after it.' As for weight-loss or metabolic benefits, she's less convinced. 'There's no evidence that drinking this instead of eating breakfast will change the way your body processes energy.' But if you have room for the calories, Applegate says there's nothing wrong with starting your day with a cup. ∎

ROCKET FUEL
Get your run off
to a flying start

Photography **Johanna Parkin**

PERFECT
TIMING

When you eat something is almost as important as what it is. Use this guide to match your meals to your training

R
unners are not average citizens. We are different to the sedentary folk for whom dietary recommendations were created. We need more calories and protein. More carbohydrates. We need more nutrients in general. And runners covet foods that never figure in government recommendations — like carbohydrate and protein drinks and energy gels.

That's why we've designed this food plan, aimed specifically at runners, that as well as being tasty, will help keep you on the move.

HOW TO GET YOUR TIMINGS RIGHT

Many runners know exactly what they should eat and when they should eat it. It's the practical application of this theory that messes them up. You are either ravenous when you don't want to be (during training) or not hungry when you should be (immediately after training). The problem is when you are planning your run around a busy work schedule, your brain, leg muscles and stomach aren't always in sync.

An early morning run, for example, can leave you feeling fatigued during your working day. A midday training session may become no more than an afterthought if hunger overrides your motivation. And an after-work jaunt may press your dinnertime perilously close to your bedtime.

If you are looking for ways to get back into sync, read on. The following advice will help coordinate your meals with your training schedule, based on the time of day you run. ▸

DAWN PATROLLING

To eat, or not to eat? That is the eternal question of those who like to run as the sun is coming up over the horizon. The answer is, if you can, you should fuel up before you set out on your morning run. This performs two important functions. Firstly, your muscles receive an energy supply to help you power through the run. Second, your entire body, especially your brain, receives the fuel and nutrients it needs for optimal functioning.

It shouldn't be a surprise to find studies support this and that eating before a run boosts endurance compared with fasting for 12 hours. People who eat before working out rate the exercise as being better, yet less rigorous, compared with those of non-eaters.

That said, not everyone can eat before a morning run. If you're the type of person who sleeps until the minute before you head out the door, you might not be able to fit in a meal. Also, eating too close to your run may spoil it by causing nausea or cramps. On the other hand, if you're a true early bird, you may eat breakfast, read the paper and wash up before you head out.

Here are some refuelling tips and strategies for all types of morning exercisers:

EARLY RISERS

Choose high-carb foods that are low in fat and moderate in protein. Aim for about 400-800 calories, which will fuel your training without making you feel sluggish. Drink about half a pint of water two hours before your run to offset sweat loss. Try one of these 400-800 calorie pre-run breakfasts:
■ Two slices of toast, a yoghurt and a piece of fruit.
■ Cereal with skimmed or semi-skimmed milk and fresh fruit.
■ A toasted sesame-seed bagel topped with low-fat cheese and a sliced tomato.

LATE SLEEPERS

Most runners will fall into this category: they don't have time to eat and digest a full meal before heading out. If you fall into this camp, experiment to see what you can stomach before you train. But you could start off by trying:
■ Have 250ml of any carbohydrate drink.
■ An energy gel washed down with water.

THE THIRD WAY

If neither of these options sits well with you just before a run, then try fuelling up the night before with a large dinner. As long as you are not planning a long or intense run in the morning, a high-carbohydrate evening meal should still power you right through your pre-breakfast session. Try one of these classics:
■ Macaroni cheese
■ Bangers and mash
■ Spaghetti carbonara

> FUEL UP THE NIGHT BEFORE WITH A BIG DINNER

RECOVER RIGHT

Whatever time you manage to get out the door, your body needs calories from carbs, protein and other nutrients once you've finished. A recovery meal will help fuel your morning at work, preventing post-run fatigue. Eat within an hour of your training and be sure to include both carbs and protein. Some options include:
■ A fruit smoothie made with a tablespoon of protein powder.
■ Eggs on wholewheat toast, juice or fresh fruit.
■ Leftovers from dinner – pasta, soup, chilli or even vegetarian pizza are proven winners.

THE LUNCH CROWD

People who run during their lunch hours sometimes find hunger gets the better of them. That's because if you ate breakfast at 6am, you've gone about six hours without any food at all. By noon, your fuel from breakfast is long gone and your blood sugar may start to dip, causing tiredness and even dizziness. Rather than increasing the size of your breakfast – which could just leave you feeling tired and sluggish – you should bring

a light, pre-run snack to eat while at work. Eat one to four hours before your run to allow enough time for food to leave your stomach, and consume 100-400 calories, depending upon your body size and how much you had for breakfast. Select foods that are high in carbs, low in fat and moderately rich in nutrients. Try these mid-morning snacks to help keep you on the go and make sure you don't go into the red when doing your midday run:
■ A breakfast or energy bar with five grams of fat or less.
■ One slice of wholemeal toast topped with fruit spread.
■ A 75g serving of dried fruit with a glass of vegetable juice.
■ One packet of instant porridge made with skimmed or semi-skimmed milk.

FEELING FRUITY
Brighter ideas for daytime dining

RECOVER RIGHT

The obvious problem with lunch-hour exercise is that you don't have time for lunch. But you need fluid and food to recover and fuel your brain for the rest of the day. Packing lunch becomes a must – unless you have a work canteen where you can grab food for desktop dining. A well-rounded packed lunch can be put together in less time than you might think. Try these tips:
■ Buy items that save time, such as yoghurts, raisins, nuts and health bars.
■ Always add fruit. Toss one or two pieces of fruit in your lunch bag for a reliable source of nutrient-packed carbohydrate.
■ Make the most of those evening meal leftovers. Choose any food from the previous night's dinner that you've already packed in a sealed container ready for you to transport and reheat whenever you like.

BETTER LATE THAN NEVER

After a stressful day at the office, there's nothing quite like a run to burn off some of the tension. The problem is you don't always feel like heading out the door if you're hungry or just exhausted. If you do manage to run, sometimes you will return home feeling so ravenous that you end up gorging yourself on anything in sight as you make your evening meal. Then you might eat your dinner as late as 9pm and end up going to bed with a full stomach.

The main rule to stick to if you are going for an evening run is to eat healthily during the day to avoid any intestinal upset that might thwart your training plans. Also eat often and enough that you're adequately fuelled for your session to avoid the "I'm too hungry" excuse. Evening ▷

exercisers may also want to keep the following in mind:

■ Never skip breakfast. Try to eat at least 500 calories for your morning meal. For example, throw together a fruit smoothie made with yoghurt, fruit and juice while you are preparing your toast. Or try cereal topped with nuts, skimmed milk and a piece of fruit.

■ Make lunch your main meal of the day. Focus on high-quality protein, such as fish, tofu, lean beef or lamb, chicken or bread with cooked grain, along with fresh fruit. A smoothie, juice or natural yoghurt drink are also great, healthy lunch foods.

■ Always eat a mid-afternoon snack. Around three hours before your run, have some fruit or an energy bar together with half a pint of water.

RECOVER RIGHT

Eating the right stuff after an evening run can be tricky. You need to replace lost sugars, but you don't want to overload on carbs so much that they get turned to fat while you sleep. Follow these tips to make your supper super:

■ Eat moderately at dinner. Some people worry about eating too close to bedtime because they fear the calories will go straight to their fat cells. That's simply not true. Your body will actually use those calories to stockpile fuel in your muscles. On the other hand, if you eat more calories than your body burns off – no matter what time of day or night – your body will

store the excess as fat. The key is not to eat more calories than you've used during your workout.

■ Drink more fluids when possible. Grab a drink as soon as you step back through the door after your run. And keep drinking as you prepare your meal (no, not red wine). This helps replace sweat loss and may prevent you trying to eat all the contents of your kitchen cupboards in one big go.

■ Try not to eat anything an hour or so before bed to avoid indigestion that can interfere with sleep and hamper your recovery.

REFUELLING ON THE GO

Sometimes you need more than just food beforehand. If your runs last longer than an hour use energy bars, gels or drinks to refuel during your run. Because these foods contain easily digestible carbs, they make great pre- and post-run snacks as well. Consume about 30-60g of carbs during each hour of running (most bars contain 30g or more of carbs; most gels contain about 25g). Simple foods such as jelly babies, fig rolls, dried fruit and honey can also supply fast, easily digestible carbs while also being a motivational sweet treat. Just don't overdo them or you'll negate your gains.

SERVING *SENSE*

Hold the fusilli! A serving isn't as hefty as most people think (or hope). Here are a few examples:

■ **Complex carbs** 100g of cooked pasta, beans, couscous or other grains (about the size of a computer mouse); one slice of bread; 25g of healthy cereal.

■ **Vegetables** 200g of raw leafy vegetables (about the size of a cricket ball).

■ **Fruit** One medium piece of fruit (about the size of a tennis ball); 250ml of juice; 100g of chopped or mixed fruit.

■ **Calcium** One pint of milk; 200g of yoghurt; two slices of cheese.

■ **Protein** 50-75g of fish or lean meat (about the size of a deck of cards); two eggs.

■ **Healthy foods** 25g of nuts; an eighth of avocado; two teaspoons of olive oil.

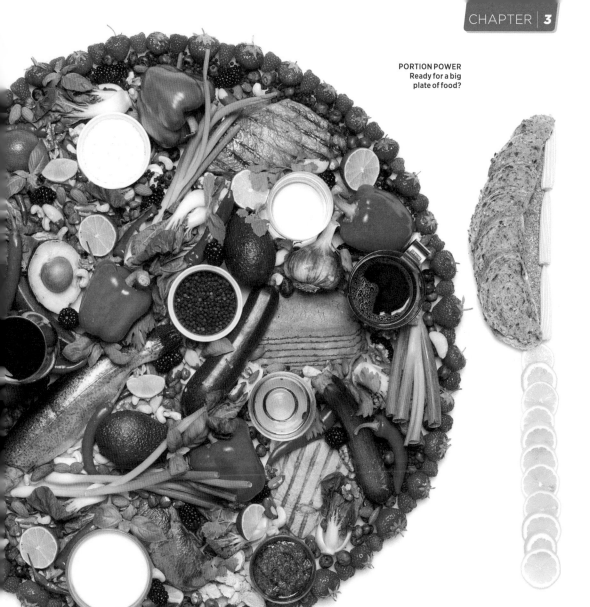

PORTION POWER
Ready for a big
plate of food?

IN **SUMMARY**

The four easy-to-remember golden rules of tailoring your nutrition to your workout plan

If you run in the morning
try to eat at least an hour
before you begin. If you
don't have time to digest
properly, experiment with
carb drinks and energy
gels or eat a large meal
the night before.
If you run at lunch, have
a mid-morning snack and
pack your own lunch to eat
afterwards at your desk.

If you run in the evening
eat well during the day to
prevent post-work
slothing. Make lunch
your main meal and eat
healthy snacks throughout.

And remember, eating
junk food occasionally is
not the end of the world. If
it's not out of control, don't
beat yourself up. Enjoy the
rare indulgence. ■

REFRESHER
COURSE

A guide to how much – and what – to drink during
your training runs, no matter what the distance

While it's
important to
stay hydrated
during exercise,
it's impossible to create
one-size-fits-all drinking
guidelines. Your weight,
sweat rate, effort level, and
of course the temperature,
all affect how much you
should drink. But that doesn't
mean you should leave your
hydration plan to chance.
These strategies can help
ensure you drink the right
amount before, during and
after every run.

BEFORE
One of the best ways to limit
dehydration during a run is to
drink enough beforehand.
'Checking your urine pre-run
is an easy way to see
if you're hydrated,' says Dr
Lewis Maharam, former
medical director of the Rock
'n' Roll race series. 'If it's the
colour of iced tea, you need
to drink more. If it's a pale
lemonade or straw colour,
you're nicely hydrated.' With
the exception of alcoholic
drinks, which are dehydrating,
all beverages, including water,
sports drinks, coffee, tea, juice
and milk, can help keep you
hydrated throughout the day.

DURING
If you're out for an 18-miler,
drinking mid-run is a no-
brainer. But what if you're
going for an hour? Or doing
intervals? 'There have been
a range of recommendations
over the past two decades,'
says Maharam. 'The newest
brings us back to basics:
drink to your thirst.' It's
advice backed up by the

International Marathon
Medical Directors Association
and Dr Tim Noakes, author of
*Waterlogged: The Serious
Problem of Overhydration in
Endurance Sports* (Human
Kinetics). 'Your thirst
mechanism is exquisitely
tuned to your body,' says
Noakes. 'If you drink when
you're thirsty, you'll keep your
body adequately hydrated.'
The American College of
Sports Medicine recommends
drinking enough so you don't
lose more than three per cent
of your weight through sweat
– lose more than that and
your performance starts to
falter. One way to figure out
how much you lose during an
hour of running is to weigh
yourself naked pre- and post-
run (without drinking
anything during the run). The
number of kilograms you lose
equates to your sweat loss in
litres. So, if you lost a kilo,
you sweated a litre of fluid.
   On runs longer than 60
minutes, sports drinks are
a good idea. They have carbs
for energy, and electrolytes
such as sodium and
potassium, which are lost
through sweat but are
integral to nerve and muscle
function.

AFTER
When you come in from a run,
drink until you're satisfied.
If your face has white salt
streaks on it post-run, it
means you've lost quite a bit
of sodium, so it's best to have
a sports drink, water with an
electrolyte tablet in it, or
water along with food that
contains sodium. After
especially long or hard runs,

you also need protein to help
your muscles heal. That's
why recovery drinks are ideal
– they provide protein and
fluid to help you rehydrate.
'Chocolate milk is a great
choice,' says Maharam. 'The
carbs-to-protein ratio is
perfect for recovery.' ■

HIGH-OCTANE *FUELS*

PRE-RUN

Coffee or tea
Several studies show
caffeine can boost
endurance.

Coconut water
The liquid found in
coconuts is packed with
the electrolyte
potassium.

MID-RUN

Sports drinks
Carbs provide mid-run
energy; sodium helps
replace electrolytes lost
through sweat.

Electrolyte tablets
A low-calorie way
to replenish lost
electrolytes; the sodium
in them stimulates thirst
to promote drinking.

POST-RUN

Chocolate milk
This has the ideal
carbs-to-protein ratio
for muscle recovery.

Smoothies
Fruit and yoghurt
provide protein and
antioxidants.

Photography **Adam Voorhes**

A FULL TANK
A good nutrition
strategy can make
a big difference

A GOOD NUTRITIONAL
STRATEGY IS AS IMPORTANT
AS REGISTERING FOR
A RACE ON TIME OR
DOING UP YOUR LACES

FUELLING YOUR *FIRE*

Run out of gas during a long run and you will crash to the tarmac. The perfect nutrition strategy of personal mobile pit stops will have you clocking faster times and feeling stronger

Photography **Getty**

Y ou've been running for months. You've spent more early mornings in trainers than you have tucked up in bed; you've done short runs, long runs, quick ones and slow ones, all of them at paces ranging from "race" to "rather not actually, thanks". You've burnt through three pairs of shoes and set new personal bests along the way. You may be planning to enter a race, or simply to run faster for your own entertainment.

But despite all the hours of hard work, you won't reach that finish line or see the time you were hoping for on your watch if you're not prepared to provide your body with the fuel it needs along the way. A good nutrition strategy is as important to your success as registering for a race on time or doing up your laces. The time to start forming your

mid-run habits is a long time before you're limbering up on the start line. It should start a few weeks into your schedule of marathon preparation — and should become a habit for all long runs.

WALL TO FALL
Regardless of whether it's a gel, a drink, a bar or even just sweets that you're knocking back on the move, you're doing it for one very visceral reason — the wall. The wall is what distance runners hit, traditionally somewhere after 18 miles. They feel light-headed and utterly without energy. In short, they would much prefer to just potter off home for a lie down than carry on going.

Is this you? And, if so, what happened? How could collapsing into a sofa or a bath become a viable alternative to strong running?

When your body senses that your easily accessible reserves of carbohydrate energy have fallen to 40 or 50 per cent, it starts to use its fat as a source of fuel. It simply cannot let your blood sugar reserves empty completely, because your brain relies on them.

The trouble is that fat can't be turned into energy nearly as fast as blood sugar can, so your body becomes forced to either slow down or increase its effort dramatically to maintain the same speed. In both cases, you'll find yourself breathing more heavily, because fat conversion requires more oxygen.

"When running you burn through your main source of stored energy — glycogen — very quickly, and the faster you go the more quickly you burn it," says coach Nick Anderson. "With shorter distances, 5-10km say, you need to remain hydrated for optimal performance, but you haven't got to worry about depleting your carbohydrate stores completely.

"However, once you're out there for longer than 90 minutes you can expect to see a depletion of those glycogen stores. You will slow down dramatically and hit what is known as the wall."

So, very simply put, if your body runs out of glycogen, it has no fuel left and to keep running it has to resort to its only other fuel source — stored fats. Processing stored fats requires a lot more oxygen, so you slow down to a jog or even a walk so that less of the oxygen you breathe in goes to your muscles and more is available to break down the energy. From the wall onwards it's a mental battle to the end of your run.

You don't want to hit the wall. It's not a clever name — walls hurt and this one will, too. Fortunately, with the right nutrition you don't have to experience the full horror of the face-brick interface. In fact, by maintaining your glycogen levels your face need never come near anything vaguely brick-like.

"It's a mix of people running too hard and not using the right nutrition," says Anderson. "Someone who has a good nutrition strategy will run even splits throughout a long run."

Fundamentally, your nutrition strategy for any long run is to take on board carbohydrates every 40-45 minutes that you're on the road. Remember that and stick to it. Whatever distance you're running, if you're going to be running for longer than an hour you should be putting in some fuel. So for a marathon you may need 4-5g, for a half-marathon perhaps just 2g and on a 10K most people will have finished before your body needs anything. The products are very rapidly absorbed as your body is, understandably, extremely keen to grab what

it needs. Just don't wait for a telegram telling you quite how desperately it needs it.

"The classic mistake is to feel woozy and then reach for a drink or a gel," explains Anderson. "They are both packed with sugars as well as complex carbs, both of which work as efficiently as each other. But if you wait until halfway through a marathon to take something on, it's far too late for you to benefit."

EATING ON THE GO
What you take on is more than a matter of mere taste. A myriad of sport-specific products exists, each one vying for that place in your race-day kit bag. But all products are not created equal. Oh no. You can choose from carbohydrate gels to isotonic drinks; energy bars to the famous Jelly Babies; every one offering different combinations of nutritional benefit to your body while it's busy setting your personal best for you.

■ **Drinks** The original performance enhancer is still as good as they always have been. They are easy to take on and quickly absorbed thanks to their liquid format, and they replace the minerals you lose through sweat when you're putting in the hard yards. "Isotonics are a closer match to your body's fluids, so get to work immediately," says track and field coach Chris Husbands. "Intersperse with water, though, as some can be too dense for comfortable digestion."

■ **Gels** If the race organisers are only offering water on the day of the race then you should olan ahead and tuck some gels safely into your pockets to ensure you have access to the energy, electrolytes and vitamins you'll need along the way. Again, just watch your hydration levels. "The efficiency and convenience of gels have resulted in many competitors drinking less during races, causing dehydration and, ironically decreased performance,"

RUNNING FUEL
Keeping energy levels topped up when on the road

PRE-RACE *EATS*

Starting with a full tank is as important as fuelling during your run or race

THE DAY BEFORE
The aim is to top up your glycogen stores and stay hydrated. Follow this checklist to avoid any pitfalls.

Graze
Eat little and often throughout the day. Choose high carbohydrate, low-fat, moderate-protein meals to avoid overburdening your digestive system.

Avoid feasting
It's not a good idea to gorge the night before as this can play havoc with your digestive system and keep you awake.

Stick with familiar foods
Eat only foods that you know agree with you and eat them in normal-sized amounts. Don't try anything new.

Avoid alcohol
Sounds obvious but beyond the hangover and queasy stomach alcohol is a diuretic and, if you have even a bit too much, you'll feel well below par.

Beware of the gas
Avoid gas-forming foods such as baked beans and other pulses, cruciferous vegetables (broccoli, Brussels sprouts, cauliflower), bran cereals and spicy foods.

Take to the bottle
Keep a water bottle handy so you remember to drink throughout the day. This is especially important if you are travelling to the race venue on this day, as it's easy to forget to drink.

RACE DAY
By now, your muscle glycogen stores should be fully stocked and you'll feel ready to go. All that remains to be done before the race is to top up your liver glycogen stores at breakfast time as this is normally depleted overnight.

Eat 2-4 hours before
A carb-rich pre-event meal means you'll begin fully fuelled and ready to get to fly from the start.

Drink enough
Have at least 500ml of water or a sports during the two hours before the race, then another 125–250ml just before you start the race.

says Nick Mitchell, head coach and founder of Ultimate Performance (upfitness.co.uk).

■ **Sweets** The gel or liquid format has taken over from tablets or chews, being more efficient and easier to digest. That's not to say that something sweet doesn't have its nutritional merits. "Eating Jelly Babies or Haribo towards the end of a run will do everything a gel does a little slower but taste a lot better," says Anderson. "If you're out there for 3-4 hours or longer then you're entitled to a treat."

■ **Bars** In theory, these are the absolute best, packing in the most carbohydrate and therefore providing the most energy. But — and this is worthy of note — they can be difficult to eat because of fiddly wrappers and breaking into pieces while you are on your run. "Cyclists use them all the time because their upper body is static," says Anderson. "And ultra-runners can slow down for the time it takes to eat and digest one." Running puts the stomach walls under constant stress, so giving them something solid to deal with can have less than favourable results if you're not used to them.

PREPARE TO SUCCEED

On a pragmatic level, if your body is not well acquainted with the product you choose then it will be unable to extract the optimal amount of energy at exactly the time when it needs it. So, regardless of which carbohydrate source you choose, it's vital to practise on-the-move refuelling during training, and especially before a race. Different events have different sponsors, meaning differently branded cups are going to be out at the hydration points.

"You've got to make a decision based on the event are you training for and what is available on the day," says Anderson. "London has Lucozade; the Great North Run Powerade. If you're not an elite athlete, you can't put your own drinks out, so you need to practise with what the specific sponsors will be providing."

That done, take a firm hold of the things you can control — the gels, bars or sweets you intend to carry with you. Practise taking on board your carbohydrates during the long runs of your weekly training but, if you are planning on being at a start line any time soon, do it at race pace. Your body needs to adapt to digesting at speed, as that's exactly what it will have to do three-quarters of an hour after the start on the big day. Which is not a time to give your stomach any surprises.

Finally, on the morning of any race, check the weather as it influences more than what top you wear. On a hot day you burn through your glycogen more quickly, which means adapting the timings of your fuelling to come five to 10 minutes more often, every 30 minutes in extreme cases. But it's not just the scorchers you have to worry about. "On a very cold day people don't take on very much at all," says Anderson. "They don't think they're sweating but the moisture is being absorbed by technical clothing. On a very cold day you still need a hydration and nutrition strategy."

Pick your product, practise with it in training, and stick to your strategy. The rules of mid-race nutrition are simple and based upon even more straight-forward biological principles. Your body uses energy to power you onwards, if that runs out you will have nothing to go on besides grim determination which is nowhere near as tasty as one of these treats.

PREMIUM FUEL
Choose your brand
and stick to with
it on race day

WHAT YOU TAKE ON IS MORE THAN A MATTER OF MERE TASTE. REMEMBER, ALL PRODUCTS ARE NOT EQUAL

WHAT'S IN YOUR **BAR**

The not-so-secret ingredients that help fight fatigue on your run

Energy drinks or gels will contain glucose, maltodextrin and perhaps fructose to deliver fast energy. Sodium and potassium are often also present to replace lost electrolytes and speed rehydration. However, many products on the market now also include these extra ingredients designed to enhance performance:

Caffeine As evidence stacks up that caffeine can boost athletic

performance, so more manufacturers include it in their energy products. Don't worry — it won't dehydrate you, and may genuinely help you.

Guarana This stimulant is a Brazilian plant. It contains caffeine and acts in a similar way. It is available in many forms, such as chocolate bars, powder, capsules, and syrup

B-vitamins (Including niacin, thiamin and pantothenic acid). This

group of vitamins helps your body to release energy from food and drink, so that it is used during races.

Minerals (Often magnesium, calcium). These help with muscle contractions and nerve function, helping your body work smoother.

Antioxidants Vitamins A (including carotenes), C and E are antioxidant vitamins that may be included in your energy

products. They'll also help to protect your immunity.

Protein Though carbs are the best energy source for runners, protein can also be used to fuel your muscles, and helps to protect them from damage caused by long sessions.

Amino acids These are the building blocks of protein, and are used for energy and fight fatigue which can hinder you towards the end of a run.

PROTEIN
SHAKE-UP

Are you getting enough protein? Runners need more of it – and more often – than non-athletes. Here's how to ensure you're hitting your target

Compared with sedentary people, runners need a lot more protein. If you run for an hour most days, you need about 0.6g of protein per pound of weight (run more and your needs go up even more), compared with 0.36g for couch potatoes. That means a 150lb (68kg) runner requires 90g a day. But don't try loading up at one or two meals; research shows spreading your

BUILD MUSCLE
As your training mileage and intensity increase, your body utilises protein to build new muscle fibres making them stronger and bigger. It also plays a key role in building mitochondria, which act like furnaces inside muscle cells, burning fuel during runs. The harder you train, the more you need in order to burn fuel efficiently.

LOSE WEIGHT
In a study by the US Army, dieters who ate twice the recommended daily allowance (RDA) of protein while cutting calories lost more fat and kept more lean muscle than those who stuck with the RDA. Another study from the University of Missouri in the US found that eating a high-protein breakfast (with 35g of protein), as opposed to one low in protein (with 13g), curbed participants' appetites later in the day and reduced cravings for high-fat, high-sugar snacks in the evening.

GET THE BEST
Runners need to select quality protein that contains branched-chain amino acids (BCAAs). These acids are key in supporting muscle recovery. Leucine in particular helps stimulate protein building after exercise. Eggs, chicken, pork and lean beef are some of the richest sources of leucine. You can also get it from fish, soy and whey, a type of protein found in dairy that the body can quickly digest and use to rebuild muscle after a workout. Legumes, nuts and wholegrains also supply protein in smaller amounts. Eating a variety of these foods will provide a balance of amino acids.

Photography **Getty**

PRO *TIMING*

Eat protein at the right times to maximise its performance benefits.

RISE AND SHINE

Sports performance nutritionist Krista Austin, who has a doctorate in exercise physiology and sports nutrition, says that runners who front-load their day with more protein set themselves up for a more stable supply of energy, wind up feeling more satiated during the rest of the day, and enhance their moods. On easy days, eat 35 per cent protein and 45

per cent carbs. On days when you're going hard or long, make it 25 per cent protein and 60 per cent carbs. Austin says that overall, runners need to up their protein intake for breakfast on most training days.

THE RECOVERY WINDOW

Protein is imperative for muscle repair and growth. Runners need to time protein intake to hit the 30-minute post-workout recovery window. Austin recommends that this meal or snack contain 25-30g of protein for a 8.5st runner (scale to your own weight).

DAIRY PROTEIN PRE-BED

While some studies have linked weight

gain and late-night eating patterns, an extensive review by the *British Medical Journal* showed that this correlation only exists if you are eating too much or making poor food choices. Eating a protein-stocked snack before hitting the pillow will do your training a favour – it's a bonus recovery window to stimulate muscle repair and growth. An 8.5st runner should ingest 20-25g of protein, and opt for dairy: the enzymes from dairy enhance the benefits of this nightly protein. Ever-popular skimmed chocolate milk mixed with some protein powder is the perfect mix of dairy, protein and sugar to aid restoration. Drink it right before bed to ensure complete recovery and a more productive run tomorrow.

ONE *DAY*

What a runner's quality protein consumption looks like

■ **BREAKFAST TIME**
160g porridge oats with 240ml plain kefir, 1 tbsp honey, 40g walnuts and 30g dried tart cherries or 4-egg omelette with spinach, tomato and 2 Quorn sausages.

■ **POST-RUN**
Smoothie made with a scoop of whey protein powder, 150g strawberries, 1 banana, and ice or an apple and 225g low-fat cottage cheese.

■ **LUNCH TIME**
350ml black bean soup topped with greens, 1 slice wholemeal toast with 2 tbsp hummus, and 200ml semi-skimmed milk.

■ **DINNER TIME**
120g grilled salmon, 200g roasted butternut squash, 150g steamed green beans and 185g cooked quinoa.

■ **BEFORE BED**
500ml skimmed chocolate milk (add protein powder if desired).

SPEED YOUR RECOVERY

Bounce back faster from every training session using only your knife and fork

Recovering quickly is the key to making improvements, and the most important factor in that recovery is nutrition. So we asked the nutrition scientists who spend their days formulating recovery products to explain the physiological processes involved and the nutrients your body needs to accelerate them.

THE GOLDEN WINDOW

The 30 minutes immediately after exercise are crucial for recovery. 'Your body is more receptive because it has seen the exercise as a threat and wants nutrients to rebuild,' says Luke Heeney, director of new products at sports nutrition company Science in Sport (SiS). 'It's about maximising that opportunity by giving your body what it needs most.'

REFUEL

'In recovery mode, you're trying to replace the carbohydrates you've used as effectively as possible,' says Heeney. 'So you want a molecule size that empties from the stomach quickly.' What delivers, fast? 'In food sources, look at the glycaemic index (GI),' says Emma Barraclough, senior sports nutritionist at SiS. 'This is a score from 0-100, with glucose scoring 100 as the sugar that's released most quickly into the bloodstream. While in your everyday diet you want low-GI foods, in the post-exercise recovery window, you want high-GI foods to replenish muscles quickly. Look for "white" carbohydrates: white bread, white rice, white pasta.

'We use a maltodextrin in SiS REGO rapid recovery products, as its GI creates a fast release of carbohydrate into the bloodstream, and the ideal level of insulin response to trigger the replenishment of glycogen stores,' says Heeney. 'Maltodextrin is a chain of glucose units rather than a single unit. You can extract them from many sources of carbohydrate, but ideally you want a source high in amylopectin, as this is what contains the glucose units. These are known as waxy starches. We extract from corn, but potato starch, barley and oats are also good sources. Oaty porridge is good, too, though the energy won't release as quickly as it will coming from a recovery drink.'

In terms of quantity, your intake should be, 'in line with the rate at which your body can metabolise carbohydrates', says Heeney. 'This varies between 0.8g and 1.1g a minute.'

REBUILD

Next, think protein. 'We have a constant natural breakdown of protein,' says Barraclough. 'But exercise increases this through stress on the muscles, tearing fibres as we perform movements.' So you need protein to repair and rebuild, but not all protein is created equal. 'Look for a protein source with a complete amino acid profile, containing all 20 of these essential building blocks,' says Heeney. In the post-exercise 'golden window', you also want something that will be digested and transported to your muscles fast. 'Both whey and soy have complete amino acid profiles, and are digested quickly,' says Heeney. 'We use soy to avoid lactose-intolerance issues associated with whey, but they're both rapidly absorbed and contain all the amino acids.' Soy beans and soy milk are good food options.

Words **Joe Mackie** Photography **Studio33**

REHYDRATE

'Rehydration is key to facilitating the body's natural recovery processes,' says Barraclough. 'You need sufficient fluid in your body to transport waste products out of the muscles and deliver recovery nutrients and electrolytes.' Plain water isn't your best option, though. 'You'll retain fluid better if you take it in with electrolytes,' says Barraclough. 'If you drink only water you'll stimulate your kidneys to get rid of some of that fluid to rebalance your salt and sugar levels. It'll take longer to properly rehydrate and you may start your next run dehydrated.'

REBALANCE, REPAIR AND REINFORCE

'Electrolytes such as sodium, potassium and calcium are also used in energy production,' says Barraclough. 'And they're depleted when you run, through sweating and being used in energy metabolism, so they must be replaced to restore normal function.'

Antioxidant vitamins, such as A, D and C, are also needed to combat oxidative stress in your muscles. 'Oxidative stress occurs during exercise and it adds to muscle damage, so part of your recovery is getting rid of it,' says Barraclough.

'We also add some other key vitamins and minerals to our recovery formulas to take advantage of that 30-minute receptive window,' says Heeney. 'Vitamin B6 has been proven to help reduce fatigue, zinc helps protein synthesis, and magnesium combats fatigue and aids normal muscle function.' You can get these the easy way via a formulated recovery product, but if you're looking to food? 'Green, leafy veg such as kale, spinach and broccoli for zinc,' says Heeney. 'And kale, tuna or sunflower seeds are good B6 sources. However you do get a slower rate of absorption from food and it's difficult to precisely judge amounts.'

Whatever your source, consider quantity. 'Your body can only deal with 20-25g of protein every two to three hours,' says Heeney. Any more than that amount cannot be stored in the body, so has to be got rid of. Rebuilding doesn't end after those crucial first 30 minutes, though. 'Muscle breakdown can last for two or three days,' says Barraclough. 'That's why you feel Delayed Onset Muscle Soreness [DOMS], and you need to address this period as well as immediate recovery.' Keep feeding your body 20-25g of protein every two to three hours with foods such as soy beans, fish and chicken,

and prepare to recover as you sleep. 'Before bed, take in 20g of protein in the form of slow-release casein, giving your body a protein supply to work with through the night,' says Heeney. Milk is your go-to natural source. 'Eighty per cent of milk protein is casein,' says Heeney. And milk has another rebuilding ace up its sleeve – its 20 per cent whey protein content. 'A key amino acid in whey is leucine,' says Barraclough. 'It stimulates muscle-protein synthesis, so not only does milk give you the building blocks, it also tells your muscles to make more.' Down half a pint of skimmed or semi-skimmed. 'They're just as high in protein, but you avoid the saturated fat,' says Heeney.

THE SUPER
DIET

Slim down and speed up with these nutrient-packed healthy foods and drinks

When we runners hear the term 'superfoods', a list of exotic ingredients often comes to mind. Kelp noodles, anyone? But foods don't have to be obscure to be super. Take the humble lentil, which packs a massive payload of nutritional power into a tiny package. Or consider the marvel of perfect protein that is the egg. And these foods aren't just nutritionally super: they can also help you lose weight. That lentil can rev your calorie-burning engine. And eggs can hold off hunger till lunch. The 11 superfoods over the next four pages provide key nutrients runners need and also help you stay lean by boosting metabolism, burning fat or keeping you feeling full for longer.

BOOST METABOLISM

BEANS
As well as being full of hunger-reducing fibre and protein, beans pack another weight-loss superpower: resistant starch. Foods high in this nutrient (a type of carb that passes undigested through your intestine) may force your body to use extra energy to try to break them down. Researchers at the University of Colorado, US, found that adults who ate meals containing resistant starch had higher post-meal metabolic rates and that resistant starches may also help control appetite.
GET THE BOOST Purée beans with garlic and a splash of oil to make a healthy dip for veggies.

LENTILS
These tiny legumes are metabolic powerhouses. Like beans, they contain resistant starch, says Marjorie Nolan Cohn, nutritionist and author of *Overcoming Binge Eating For Dummies* (John Wiley & Sons).

Lentils are also rich in iron – if you're deficient in this mineral, your body is less efficient at using calories for fuel, says nutritionist Marlo Mittler.
GET THE BOOST Add lentils to salads. Make lentil soup a frequent lunch choice.

CHILLIES
These spicy peppers get their kick from capsaicin. Recent research at the University of California suggests this compound can boost post-meal calorie burn. 'Eating spicy food may also curb your urge to continue to eat,' says Cohn.
GET THE BOOST Sprinkle cayenne or chilli powder on recipes from casseroles to grilled fruit. Use jalapeño peppers in marinades.

Photography **Mitch Mandel**

BURN FAT FASTER

GRASS-FED BEEF

Not only does grass-fed beef taste better than corn-fed, it also has a better ratio of omega-3 to omega-6 fatty acids. Western diets generally contain too much omega-6 (which can be inflammatory) and too little omega-3 (which is anti-inflammatory), says Cohn. Grass-fed beef also contains lots of conjugated linoleic acid (CLA) which your body uses to build muscle. **FAT FIX** Grass-fed beef is pricey, so cut back on your red meat intake and eat grass-fed beef when you do indulge.

SESAME SEEDS

A compound in sesame seeds (and oil) called sesamin may have a fat-burning effect, says Cohn. 'It could be that it increases the production of ketones, which helps your body maintain muscle. This, in turn, burns fat.' Chemicals called lignans, also found in sesame seeds, help your liver to produce the enzymes necessary for fat metabolism. **FAT FIX** Use sesame oil in dressings. Coat chicken or fish with sesame seeds before cooking.

RED WINE

The skin of red-wine grapes contains resveratrol, a polyphenol linked to many benefits, such as a decreased risk of heart disease. We've been drinking to that for years and, says Cohn, resveratrol has also been shown to reduce the production of the stress hormones that compel your body to store fat. **FAT FIX** Not a difficult one, this; just enjoy that glass of stress-relieving, fat-burning red wine. Keep your daily consumption reasonable, though, because in this case you can have too much of a good thing.

GREEN TEA

The alternative cuppa gets its fat-burning boost from EGCG (Epigallocatechin gallate). 'This phytochemical promotes fat oxidation and thermogenesis [production of energy for digestion],' says Cohn. The green tea effect is well known, but other teas offer benefits, too: in studies reported in the *American Journal of Clinical Nutrition*, tea drinkers burned more calories and fat daily than non-drinkers. **FAT FIX** Swap your second cup of coffee for a cup of green tea. Add unsweetened iced green tea to smoothies, or mix it with your sports drink for a fat-burning caffeine boost.

FEEL FULLER

EGGS

'Eggs contain all the essential amino acids, making them a complete protein,' says Mittler. As well as delivering all the building blocks your body needs to repair and upgrade your muscles, they'll also save you battling those midmorning snack demons because the protein keeps your blood sugar from spiking and then crashing, which causes hunger.

FILL UP Hard-boil a dozen so you have a quick, easy-peel breakfast all week.

SOUP

Consuming a bowl of soup has been shown to curb your subsequent calorie intake. The effect is twofold, says Mittler: first, it fills you up, but soup's satiating effects also have to do with warmth. 'Warm liquids have a greater psychological effect on fullness than cold ones,' she adds.

FILL UP Ordering a starter when you're out to eat? Choose thinner soups instead of creamy, calorie-heavy options.

AVOCADOS

These creamy fruits are a rich source of monounsaturated fat, which is both heart-healthy and satiating. Like any fat eaten as part of a meal, avocados are last in line for digestion, so they stick with you: in a recent study at Loma Linda University in California, overweight people who ate half an avocado at lunch reported a significant decrease in the desire to eat later in the afternoon.
FILL UP Have half a sliced avocado as part of a lunch salad or spread it on a sandwich in place of less-healthy mayonnaise.

KILL THE CRAVINGS

If you simply must have a snack fix, try these tasty swaps to cut calories and fat

If you crave... **crisps**

Eat... **wasabi peas**
They've got crunch and their heat slows you down, so you eat fewer.

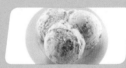

If you crave... **ice cream**

Eat... **frozen bananas**
Whirl very ripe frozen bananas in a blender. Amazingly creamy.

If you crave... **chocolate**

Eat... **one square of dark chocolate with a dried fig**
The fruit adds sweetness and chewiness. ■

POTATOES

You don't have to dump these tubers in the same bin as low-nutrient carbs such as white bread or white rice. Loaded with resistant starch (not to mention vitamin C and potassium), potatoes have staying power, keeping hunger pangs at bay two to three times longer than other starches, says Mittler.
FILL UP Top a baked spud with a drizzle of olive oil or a sprinkle of Parmesan, rather than piles of sour cream and butter.

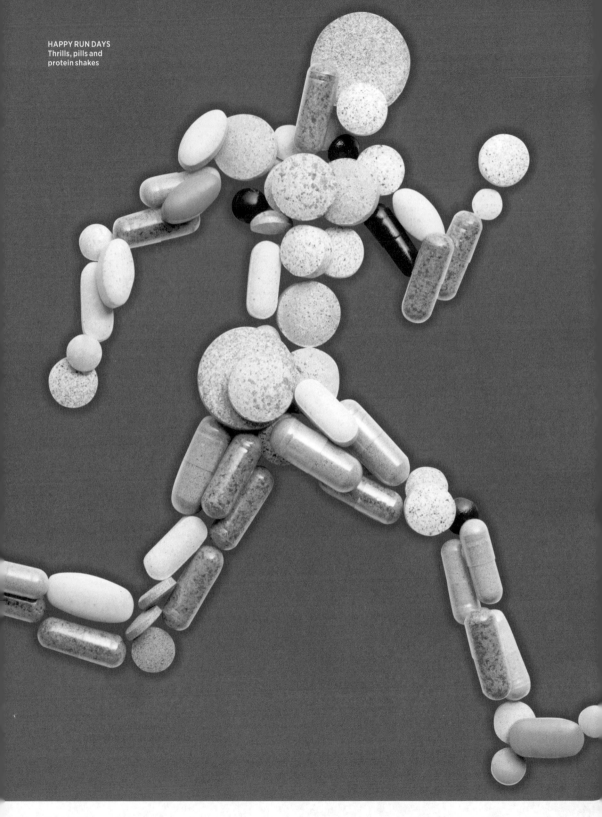

WHAT *SUPP?*

The best nutritional magic bullets that will make you a faster, healthier, more resilient runner

When it comes to upping your nutrient intake, it's tricky to separate the snake oil from the super-supp. Recent research even suggests that multi-vitamins – the UK's most commonly used supplement – could actually do more harm than good. 'They can cause stomach upsets and there is evidence in the general population that they can actually increase mortality rates,' says Professor Cathy Speed, a consultant in sports medicine (progresshealth.co.uk). It's always best to focus first on getting your necessary nutrients from a balanced diet. That said, runners are prone to a few key common nutrient deficiencies, and will also benefit from certain recovery and performance aids, which are backed up by solid science. Here are the pills, powders and potions that are worth a pop.

PERFORMANCE *GAINS*

Supplements aren't just for a keeping illness at bay, they can boost your performance when you need it

Beetroot juice
The nitrates in beetroot juice have been shown to boost stamina and speed.
Dose Have 140ml pre-race for the best results, say University of Exeter scientists.
Buy £27 for 15x70ml shots, beet-it.com

Glutamine
Research in the *Journal of Applied Physiology* found this amino acid helped athletes replenish their stocks of muscle glycogen if taken after exhaustive exercise.
Dose One tablet a day during high-mileage.
Buy £8.29 (50 tabs), hollandandbarrett.com

Creatine
This nitrogenous acid powers muscle contractions. 'Take it post-exercise to boost your next run during intense training,' says nutritionist Anita Bean.
Dose 'Mix 3-5g into a recovery shake with whey and milk,' says Bean.
Buy Creatine monohydrate, £4.19 for 250g, myprotein.com

Caffeine
The stimulant has been shown to sharpen mental focus, lower perceived exertion and boost performance.
Dose There's 75mg of caffeine in SiS GO Hydro+Caffeine effervescent tabs.
Buy £3.99 (10 fizzy tabs), scienceinsport.com

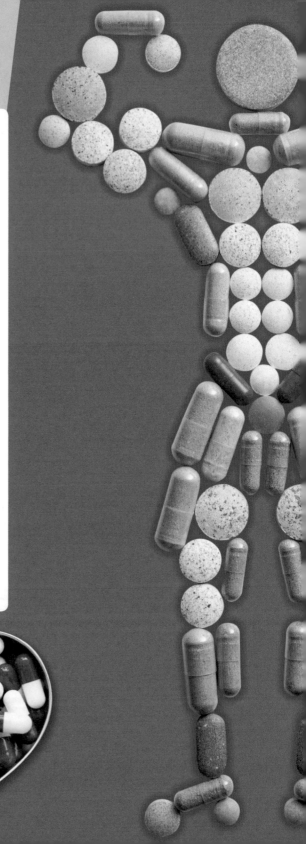

TOTAL **RECOVERY**

Supps to ensure you're ready for your next run

Whey protein
Whey helps repair and build lean muscle, and the body absorbs it faster than other proteins, so it's perfect if you struggle to stomach protein-rich food during the 30-minute 'golden window' post-run.
Dose Make a recovery shake by blending 30g of whey protein with 250ml of milk, half a frozen banana and a handful of berries to deliver the ideal 3:1 carbs-to-protein ratio.
Buy OPTI Whey Protein, £9.99 for 500g, optimusprotein.co.uk; or for a complete just-add-water formula, try SiS Whey Protein, £24.99 for 1g, scienceinsport.com

Soy protein
Isolated from soy beans, this is the best protein fix if you want to avoid milk. It's a complete protein source, so packs all the amino acids needed for muscle fibre synthesis.
Dose Add a scoop to post-run smoothies, or stir into porridge.
Buy £11.99 for 1kg, myprotein.com; or for a just-add-water formula, go for SiS ReGo Rapid Recovery, £10.80 for 500g, scienceinsport.com

Casein
Like whey, casein is derived from dairy. Yet where whey is anabolic – meaning it helps stimulate muscle fibre growth. Slow-release casein is an anti-catabolic, meaning it helps guard against muscle fibre breakdown. Older runners in particular might benefit from this.
Dose Get 27g from a 65g serving of Elivar Recover (formulated especially for athletes aged 35+).
Buy Recover, £24.99 for 900g, elivar.com

Cherry juice
This natural anti-inflammatory helps reduce muscle pain and weakness after intense sessions, according to research published in the *Scandinavian Journal of Medicine & Science in Sports*.
Dose 30ml daily, after tough races.
Buy £18.99 for 12x30ml, cherryactive.co.uk

TRAINING SUPPORT
When you need
a helping hand

INJURY **PREVENTION**

Keep yourself on the straight and narrow

Glucosamine
While there's no firm evidence on glucosamine's joint-protective effects, 'some people swear it reduces pain', says Speed. 'Try a three-month trial.' The amino sugar can work best when taken with chondroitin.
Dose One 1,500mg glucosamine tablet and one chondroitin, daily.
Buy £11.45 for both 120 tablets (glucosamine) and 90 tablets (chondroitin), healthspan.co.uk

Vitamin D
'Vitamin D deficiency is very common, particularly in winter,' says Speed. That matters because vitamin D is vital for bone health, and topping up low levels could counter muscle weakness, according to research presented to the Society for Endocrinology.
Dose Speed says deficient runners may benefit from a 1,000 IU/day cholecalciferol supplement – that's vitamin D3 in its natural form. See your GP first if possible.
Buy £5.25 (120 tabs), justvitamins.co.uk

Spirulina
Also lauded for its performance-boosting effects, this algae extract might help protect you from soft tissue injuries, too. It helped limit skeletal muscle damage in runners, in a study published in the *European Journal of Applied Physiology*.
Dose 2-4 capsules daily.
Buy £9.99 for 500mg, simplysupplements.net

SUPPORT **HEALTH**

Support your efforts and come back stronger

Colostrum
Made from the first milk a cow produces after calving, colostrum can bolster the immune system during times of intense physical and mental stress, like marathon training. Several studies suggest a few weeks of supplementation can help safeguard athletes against upper respiratory infections.
Dose Mix 3-10g with 300ml water daily.
Buy £9 for 100g, neovite.com

Iron
'Athletes training heavily for endurance events may need iron supplementation, particularly female runners,' says Speed.
Dose 200mg of ferrous sulphate, one to three times per day. Though ask your GP first as high doses of iron can be harmful.
Buy £1.99 (60 tabs), weldricks.co.uk

Fish oil
Nature's best source of omega-3, fish oil is credited for everything from keeping your blood pressure in check to promoting emotional stability. 'Have capsules if you struggle to eat enough oily fish,' says Bean. Quality varies, so find one with a combined DHA/EPA count close to 1,000mg.
Dose 2 capsules daily
Buy £25.05 (60 Triple-Strength caps), hollandandbarrett.com

Probiotics
'These could have a role for runners training at high intensity,' says Bean. 'After intense training, immune cells can be depressed for a while, leaving you vulnerable to illnesses. Evidence suggests that probiotics help counter this.'
Dose One pill, with at least two billion active cultures, two to four times daily
Buy £8.25 (90 tabs), justvitamins.co.uk ■

HOT SAUCE
Burn calories
by turning up
the heat

49 TOP FAT BURNING *TIPS*

Losing weight isn't just about doing mega mileage.
These easy diet changes will have fat falling off

Photography **Tony Briscoe Martha Pavlidou at Studio 33**

1 SWAP YOUR REGULAR CHEESE FOR GOAT'S CHEESE
It's 40 per cent lower in calories than the stuff made from cow's milk.

2 SPRINKLE ON SOME CINNAMON
Try it on your morning coffee. The spice is a powerful metabolism raiser; half a teaspoon a day is enough to burn a kilo a month.

3 SIP GREEN TEA
It contains a compound that reacts with caffeine to boost both fat oxidisation and resting metabolic rate by 20 per cent.

4 EAT BEANS
Try the cannellini, haricot or kidney varieties. People who add them to each meal are 22 per cent less likely to become obese.

5 IF IT DIDN'T GROW, WALK OR SWIM, DON'T EAT IT
Processed foods are loaded with harmful trans fats and artificial sweeteners that play havoc with your metabolic system.

6 PUT SOME TOMATOES IN YOUR SANDWICH
They keep you feeling fuller for longer, and will make you less likely to gorge on mid afternoon snacks. The fruit suppresses the hunger hormone ghrelin, which is responsible for hunger pangs.

7 HAVE A HANDFUL OF PEANUTS EVERY DAY
These will provide you with heart-healthy folates and fibre, plus the higher satiety level than other foods will stop you grazing.

8 SLICE YOUR FOOD
You'll eat 20 per cent fewer calories. People rate sliced servings as 27 per cent larger than unsliced.

9 DRINK MILK
Calcium prevents the storage of fat at a cellular level.

10 ADD CHILLI SAUCE TO YOUR MEALS
The fiery pepper will add a big kick to the dish, rev up your metabolism and help to process fats more efficiently.

11 EAT THREE 250KCAL PROTEIN-RICH SNACKS A DAY
Those who followed this simple tip were 30 per cent more likely to lose weight than those who didn't. ▶

12 DRINK SOME GRAPEFRUIT JUICE

One study showed that if you have this for breakfast every day you'll lose four and a half pounds in 12 weeks thanks to its insulin-lowering enzymes.

13 ADD LENTILS TO EACH MEAL

You'll lose over 15lb in 10 weeks. These pulses are packed with the fat-burning amino acid leucine.

14 EAT SOME POMEGRANATES

Their seed oil reduces the body's ability to store fat and they're so sweet they'll curb your desire for sugary snacks.

15 EAT MORE BERRIES

When aiming to eat more fruit it's worth being clever about what you pick. Most berries make a great choice as many other fruits contain lots of fructose, which can combine with carbohydrates to add body fat.

16 EAT HIGH-FIBRE, LOW-STARCH CARBOHYDRATES

Try raw nuts, quinoa, barley, oats and legumes such as lentils, beans and various soy products. These will regulate your insulin levels, keep you full and reduce hunger pangs throughout the day.

17 EAT SOME CHILLI CON CARNE

An enzyme in kidney beans tells the body to break down stored fat instead of carbs for energy, while the minced beef helps to boost your metabolism.

18 ADD SOME CHOPPED SPRING ONIONS TO YOUR POST-RUN MEAL

These contain chromium and can help you metabolise carbs for fuel, plus they're full of fibre and calcium, which aids weight loss.

POME-GREAT! Curb hunger and burn fat with these seed powerhouses

19 LEAVE A MAXIMUM OF THREE HOURS BETWEEN MEALS

This is the average amount of time it takes to digest a meal. Sticking to this time will also ensure your metabolic rate doesn't fluctuate.

20 EAT BREAKFAST EVERY DAY

Those who fail to kick-start their metabolism with a meal in the morning eat 100 more calories during the course of the day.

21 EAT GOOD FATS TO BURN FAT

Eggs, avocado, olive oil and the dark meat of chicken are all good for your body and studies have also shown they can help cut your the risk of heart disease.

22 SCOFF EGGS FOR BREAKFAST

They contain low-calorie protein, which is perfect for weight loss, plus they will keep you feeling full all morning.

27 DRINK A GLASS OF CARROT JUICE
Just one a day will help you lose four pounds in 12 weeks compared with non-juice drinkers. It's high in fibre and nutrients that help burn the blubber.

28 DRINK JUICE THAT HAS BITS IN IT
The fibre is processed at a slower rate, staving off hunger.

29 HAVE A DAILY GLASS OF WINE
The red kind in particular can stop you putting on weight around your belly. The antioxidant resveratrol, found in the grapes, inhibits the development of fat cells around your waistline.

30 ADD PAPRIKA TO YOUR MEALS
The mild ground red peppers have been found to contain nearly six times the vitamin C found in tomatoes, which is crucial for enabling your body to convert fat into energy.

31 SIT DOWN AT THE TABLE TO EAT
Studies have shown that you will consume a third less than when you're munching on the move.

32 SPLASH ON LOW-SALT SOY SAUCE
Research shows that soy proteins interact with the receptors in our brains that tell us we're full. The low-salt variety means you can sidestep any health downsides.

33 MAKE A SMOOTHIE FOR BREAKFAST
If you can't face much to eat when you first wake up try this recipe: blend 200g strawberries, 125ml soya milk and two teaspoons of vanilla extract for a belly-banishing drink.

34 DRIZZLE OLIVE OIL ON SALADS
Its packed full of good fatty acids that trigger the release of a hormone that tells the body it's full. ▶

23 DON'T OVERDO SPORTS DRINKS
These can contain high-GI carbs, which can increase body fat. For runs of less than one hour, drink water instead.

24 EAT POPCORN
The cinema favourite will help to lower your blood glucose levels, which, in turn, switches your body into fat-burning mode. Just make sure it's plain, air popped, not sweet or buttered.

25 DRINK SOME OOLONG TEA
Scientists at the University of Tokushima, Japan, discovered this will increase your fat burning by as much as 12 per cent.

26 EAT PINEAPPLE
Not only is it a great snack to spark your metabolism, but it also contains the enzyme bromelain, which helps to break down protein, essential for muscle recovery.

35 WAIT BEFORE HAVING SECONDS
Diving in for a second portion because you still feel hungry is a mistake. It takes 20 minutes for your stomach to send the message to your brain that it's full.

36 CHOOSE SPINACH IN FAVOUR OF OTHER GREENS
It contains double the fibre, which helps your body process fats more efficiently.

37 EAT THE PERFECT PROTEIN RATIO
To get your ideal body fat percentage eat three grams of protein per five pounds of body weight every day; only 20-30 per cent of your total calorie intake should come from fat.

38 GO FOR VINEGAR-BASED DRESSINGS
These contain acetic acid, which has been shown to speed up the rate at which your body burns fat. Add a few glugs to all your salads and sauces.

39 DILUTE THE MILK IN YOUR CEREAL
A splash of water will help to reduce the absorption of sugar and decrease fat intake.

40 EAT RED PEPPERS
They contain capsaicin, the chemical that gives them their taste and which boosts your resting metabolic rate by up to 25 per cent.

41 MAKE A BLACK BEAN SALAD
For a weight-loss meal mix together some black beans, peppers, tomatoes, onion and sweet corn with an olive oil and lemon dressing. The combination of fibre, hunger suppressants and fat-burning chemicals will shed pounds.

42 EAT A PORTION OF DAIRY EVERY DAY
Research has found that doubling calcium intake increases fat metabolism by 50 per cent.

43 INVEST IN A GRAVY SEPARATOR
It removes fat from homemade gravy, so you can pour a skimmed version over your Sunday roast.

44 DINE WITH PEOPLE WHO TEND TO EAT LESS THAN YOU
Research shows that people tend to match their food intake to the people they are eating with.

45 TAKE CONJUGATED LINOLEIC ACID (CLA) CAPSULES
Studies have shown that you'll lose up to nine per cent more fat over the course of a year than if you don't take them (£10.39, hollandandbarrett.com)

46 DON'T BANISH ALL CARBOHYDRATES
If you cut carbs from your diet completely you will only store more fat in the long run, as your body will go into 'starvation' mode. Instead, cut your carbohydrate intake by 200g a week to stimulate the appetite-repressing hormone leptin and kick-start your metabolism.

47 EAT AN APPLE
Eat it 15 minutes before a meal and you'll consume around 180 fewer calories in total.

48 EAT BLUE CORN TORTILLA CHIPS
They contain half the fat of standard crisps and also release sugar more slowly into the bloodstream, which controls insulin levels and slows weight gain (£2.69, realfoods.co.uk)

49 EAT NATURAL YOGHURT AND FISH
You don't have to eat them at the same time, but they are both great sources of iodine, which increases metabolism by encouraging the thyroid to release fat-burning hormones. ∎

Photography **Glen Montgomery**

CHAPTER **4**

HEALTH &
INJURY

Keep your body strong and avoid the ailments
and injuries that commonly afflict runners

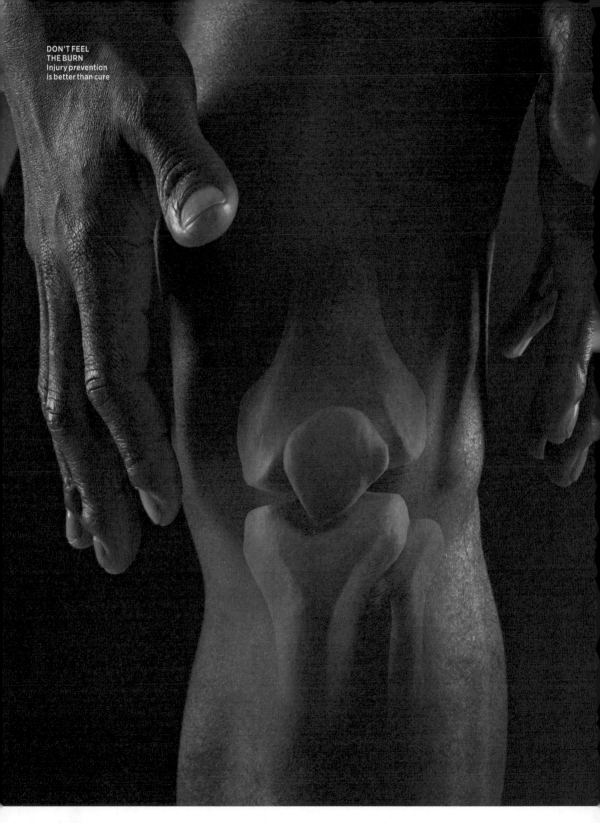

DON'T FEEL
THE BURN
Injury prevention
is better than cure

DON'T GET
HURT

Proper form, strength training and wearing the right shoes all combine to help you run strong and keep you off the sofa

Photography **Joshua Simpson** and **Guido Vitti**

I t's an all too familiar story: runner begins training. A month or so later, runner suffers twinge in knee. Runner stretches, pops ibuprofen, keeps running. A number of runs later, runner is on the sofa with an ice pack on said knee. Or hip. Or Achilles.

You'll know this story already. But just how familiar is it? Studies suggest that as few as 19 per cent or as many as 79 per cent of runners are sidelined by injury each year. Suffice to say that a lot of us are put out of action. Some – ouch – never run again.

The good news is researchers are on the hunt for an injury solution, in part thanks to the release of Christopher McDougall's *Born to Run* (Profile Books). The bestseller, which claimed modern running shoes are to blame for high injury rates, started a lively debate when it was published in 2009.

Is it the way we run? The shoes we wear? Sitting all day? Or do we keep repeating the same training mistakes: making big jumps in mileage or always running the same route?

The answer is all of the above. 'A combination of things – an anatomical issue plus a training error and the wrong shoes – can add up to injury,' says Joseph Hamill, a biomechanist at the University of Massachusetts in the US. Plus, every runner is a puzzle, with a different anatomy and injury history, says Dr Anthony Luke, director of RunSafe at the University of California in the US. 'This is why injury prevention is so challenging.'

But over the last decade, running science has shifted towards prevention. Scientists are studying uninjured runners to see who gets hurt and why. Experts generally agree that to lower your injury risk, you need a strong body, good form and the right shoes.

We take a closer look at each, offering exercises, form tweaks and shoe advice to help runners reduce injury propensity and enjoy a long, icepack-free running future.

ADD STRENGTH

I n the battle against injury, a runner's best armour is a strong body. Strong muscles, ligaments and tendons help to absorb impact forces, improve form and lead to a consistent gait.

'If muscles are weak, one footfall will not be like the rest – how your knee turns in, your hip drops and your foot pronates with each step,' says Dr Reed Ferber, director of the Running Injury Clinic at the University of Calgary in Canada. 'But with strength, these movements are the same each time, meaning your mind and body

know just what to expect.'

When a strong body runs, the brain tells the muscles to brace for impact before the foot hits the ground. The glutes and core contract to steady the pelvis and leg. The foot and ankle muscles are activated, providing a solid foundation to land upon.

But if one stabiliser isn't strong enough or isn't recruited, other muscles get overworked, and the entire chain of movement is disrupted, says Eric Orton, a running coach who created the B2R Training System, which combines strength training with form changes to reduce injury risk.

Most runners lack strength in at least one muscle group, as well as in their neuromuscular pathways – the lines of communication

between brain and body, says the biomechanist Jay Dicharry, author of *Anatomy for Runners* (Skyhorse Publishing). Strong pathways help our muscles fire more efficiently, and in quick succession, to give greater running control and stability.

These exercises from Dicharry and Orton strengthen key running muscles and those neuromuscular pathways. You can do them as a full routine or slip them sneakily into your day while watching TV, two or three times a week. If possible, do the moves barefoot.

DONKEY KICKS WITH BAR

■ **Why?** By adding a bar (or broomstick) to this old-school move, you teach your body to fire your glutes without arching your back, just as you should while running.
■ **Bonus** You're also strengthening your transverse abdominis, a stabilising muscle in your core.
■ **How?** Begin on all fours with the bar/stick across your lower back. Lift one leg back, knee bent at 90 degrees, keeping the bar still. If the bar moves, perform smaller movements. Do 50 reps on each leg.

WALL PRESS

■ **Why?** This activates your gluteus medius while you're in a bent-knee position, similar to running.
■ **How?** Stand with your left side near a wall. Bend your left knee to 90 degrees and make contact with the wall. Push your knee into the wall and hold the position, while keeping your body stable (don't press your shoulder against the wall). Hold for 20-30 seconds. Do two or three sets on each side.

SINGLE-LEG BALANCE ON FOREFOOT

- **Why?** This builds strength in the entire leg: big toes, calves, ankles and hips.
- **How?** Balance on one forefoot (try barefoot), heel raised. You should feel the side of your hip (gluteus medius) working. Hold for as long as you can, keeping upright. Rest, and do three times more.

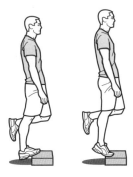

ECCENTRIC HEEL DROP

- **Why?** These strengthen calves, ankle muscles and Achilles tendons, giving a more stable landing.
- **How?** Stand on one leg on a curb or step with your heel off the edge. Lift up onto your toes, then lower down until your heel is below the step. Start with 10 on each leg. Build to 15.

CLAM SHELLS

- **Why?** These strengthen your gluteus medius for knee and pelvis stability.
- **How?** Lie on your side, legs stacked on each other. Bend both knees, with your legs and feet aligned. Open your knees like a clam shell, with your feet together. Do two sets of 30 on each side.

PLYOMETRICS

Jumping exercises increase elasticity – the springs that give running a light, bouncy feel. But they can also teach you how to minimise your impact on landing. If you're not currently strength training add these moves, after performing the other exercises in this programme, for eight weeks.

STANDING JUMP

- **How?** Use a mid-shin-height step or low bench. Standing with the step directly in front of you, jump up with both feet, landing softly. Step back down. Repeat 10-20 times.
- **Next level** When you can no longer hear your feet landing, jump up and then jump back down off the

LATERAL JUMPS

- **How?** Place a pole (or brush) on the ground and jump over it quickly side to side, spending as little time as possible in contact with the ground. Aim for three sets of 10 jumps.
- **Next level** Swap the pole for a higher item, such as a foam roller; this creates a bigger challenge.

ADD STRENGTH

CAN STRENGTH TRAINING FIX FAULTY FORM?

Strength training can improve your form by making it more stable and correcting imbalances, but it can't resolve faulty biomechanics.

If you have knock-knees, for example, you can learn to run differently via gait retraining, says Irene Davis, director of the Spaulding National Running Centre at Harvard Medical School in the US.

During two studies, Davis gave runners visual and verbal cues in order to gradually retrain their movement patterns. The runners were able to correct their flawed form as well as maintain their improved mechanics after just eight training sessions.

Davis advises using a gait-retraining specialist instead of doing it alone – as without proper feedback, it's hard to make the right corrections, she explains. Check out The Running School (runningschool.co.uk) for more info.

SWISS BALL BRIDGE

■ **Why?** To strengthen and activate your gluteus maximus and multifidus (small stabilising muscles in your back).
■ **How?** Lie on the ground with your calves on a Swiss ball, arms extended to your sides. Lift your hips so your body forms a straight line from ankles to shoulders. Hold. Once you can hold comfortably – without your hips dropping – for 60 seconds, increase the challenge...

■ **Next level**

1 Lie on your back, place your feet on the ball and cross your arms over your chest.

2 From the lifted position, do single-leg lifts, while alternating each one of your legs.

3 From the same position, rotate your body in each direction to activate more core muscles.

SWISS BALL WALKOUT

■ **Why?** This strengthens core, arm and shoulder muscles for better running posture.
■ **How?** Lie face-down, stomach on the ball, palms on the floor in a press-up position. Walk your arms out, keeping your abs tight, until your shins are on the ball. Keep your back straight. Hold for 30 seconds, building to two sets of 60 seconds.
■ **Next level**
1) Walk out until just your feet are resting on the ball.
2) From a plank position with your shins on the ball, pull your knees to your chest.

SINGLE-LEG BALANCE AND SQUAT

■ **Why?** Develops balance in your pelvis, ankles and feet for a more secure landing.
■ **How?** Balance on one foot, with your back straight, arms in running motion and weight distributed between your fore and rear foot. Then press your big toe into the floor and hold for 30 seconds. Try three sets on each leg.
■ **Next level** Standing on one leg, lower your hips back, bending your standing knee. Then push back up.

MOBILITY

The natural stress-recovery cycle of training can cause muscle fibres to knot, limiting their function and increasing injury risk. These moves increase mobility in notorious problem areas.

KNEELING HIP-FLEXOR STRETCH

■ **Why?** When you run, your leg swings from your hip. If your hip flexors are tight, the back swing is limited, leading to overstriding.
■ **How?** Kneel on one knee with your back against the inside of a door frame. Tuck your pelvis under so you feel a stretch in the front of your thigh. Hold for three minutes.

FOOT MASSAGE

■ **Why?** Your plantar fascia – a band of tissue on the foot – guides you from landing to toe-off. Limited mobility can disturb this motion.
■ **How?** Sit and put one ankle on your knee. Apply pressure on the arch of your foot. Press firmly on sore spots, then flex and extend your toes. Do this for three minutes daily until the pain is gone.

CALF SMASH

■ **Why?** Knotted calf muscles don't absorb shock too well.
■ **How?** Sit on the floor, one leg out, foam roller under it. Roll your calf over the roller, pressing when you hit painful spots. Hold until the pain goes (30-90 secs). Ask someone to press down on your shin for added pressure.

FIND THE RIGHT SHOES

Q Can shoes help prevent injury?
A Yes – they can alter your form and how repetitive forces apply to your body. Research shows the firmness of shoe cushioning can influence the stiffness of your legs, which affects how forces impact on your muscles, bones and joints. If you're in a shoe that applies forces in a way your body can manage and is a good match for your training, it can reduce injury risk. Try rotating to mix up how force is applied: a cushioned trainer for long runs, grippy shoes for trails, flats for speedwork and minimal shoes for form drills.
Dr Peter Larson, author of Tread Lightly: Form, Footwear, and the Quest for Injury-Free Running (£12.59, Allworth Press)

Q How do I know if I'm using the right shoe?
A You want a shoe that fits your biomechanics. Specialist running shop assessments are helpful, but not foolproof. My advice is to go by comfort. If it doesn't feel good, it means it's putting stress somewhere you don't want it to. If you ache after you've run, it might be a sign you're in the wrong ones.
Dr Benno Nigg, Human Performance Laboratory, University of Calgary, Canada

Q Should I switch to minimalist shoes for injury prevention?
A There's no compelling evidence that minimalist shoes reduce injury. Some runners have switched and have had great experiences, others have been hurt. Smaller, leaner runners, midfoot and forefoot strikers, and those with little injury history are most likely to make the switch without problems. Bigger runners, extreme heel strikers and anyone with chronic injury issues will take longer to adapt and may find more substantial, conventional shoes work better for them.
Dr Martyn Shorten, director of the Runner's World Shoe Lab, BioMechanica, Portland, Oregon

Q I bought a pair of minimal shoes. Now what?
A Transition gradually. Spend the first week just walking in them. The following week, start running, but wear them every other day for the first two to three weeks, and only for a mile or two. Build time and miles slowly and introduce them to harder workouts bit by bit.
Scott Douglas, author of The Complete Guide to Minimalism and Barefoot Running (£9.89, Rodale)

Q Do orthotics work?
A There has been surprisingly little research linking orthotics to injury prevention. But for people with excessive pronation or flat arches, inserts can help. Studies show an over-the-counter orthotic can be just as effective as a custom-made one, so try those first.
Dr Reed Ferber, director of the Running Injury Clinic and associate professor of kinesiology at the University of Calgary, Canada

IMPROVE YOUR FORM

I f you want to stir debate in a group of runners, bring up form. 'Minimalists' strongly believe that just as there is a correct way to swim or swing a tennis racket, there is a correct technique for running. Other experts say the way we run is individual, and messing with it only invites injury. But there is some common ground: both camps agree that certain components of form, such as good posture and proper stride (as demonstrated here by elite triathlete Andy Potts), can help prevent injuries. Here's how those elements break down.

PRE-LANDING
Just before your foot strikes the ground, your brain sends a signal to your muscles to prepare for impact. The muscles contract so that they can stabilise your joints. If this line of communication is in any way weak or slow, the muscles won't get this heads-up.

IMPACT
Some studies connect the impact forces of this touchdown phase to stress fractures and other injuries. And while midfoot and forefoot strikes minimise impact forces, experts agree that the greater hazard is overstriding – when the foot lands too far ahead of the knee.

1 RUN WITH GOOD POSTURE

What it means
Upper torso straight, lower back not arched, head directly over your shoulders.
Why it matters
Poor posture puts excess stress on your back and knees. If your back arches, your body weight tends to shift back, making you more prone to overstriding.
Try this
Strengthen your core and upper body. Practise good posture during the day. Bad postural habits carry over into your run.

2 SWING YOUR ARMS EFFICIENTLY

What it means
Arms moving forwards and backwards.
Why it matters
Arm swing affects trunk stability. An across-the-body arm swing tends to rotate the shoulders, or cause the trunk to sway, compromising core stability.
Try this
Bend your elbows to 90 degrees and let your arms swing relaxedly. Keep your elbows close to your body with your hands loose, which helps the entire body relax.

3 LAND LIGHT

What it means
Consciously landing more softly.
Why it matters
'When we try to run quietly, we make natural adjustments like shortening our stride and landing on our midfoot, which lessens impact forces,' says Dr Luke.
Try this
Run on the spot, letting your knees rise naturally, for 10 seconds. Then lean forward and run for 30m holding that posture. Repeat three times before you run.

SHOULD YOU CHANGE YOUR FOOTSTRIKE?

Some experts believe landing on your mid- or forefoot, rather than your heel, greatly reduces injury risk. Others believe you may swap one injury for another as landing on the forefoot increases impact on the calf and achilles tendon. Further complicating matters, studies show it's difficult to know how you're striking the ground (eg you think you're midfoot- or forefoot-striking but you're actually heel-striking). So some say it's better to focus on not overstriding, which is easier to judge on your own (see 'Lead With Your Hips'). **The bottom line:** If you're running injury-free, most experts say don't bother changing. But if you're chronically injured, footstrike could aid treatment and prevention. But the transition must be gradual (coach Eric Orton gets his runners to start with just 10 minutes of forefoot landing) and combined with plenty of foot, ankle and calf strengthening.

MID-STANCE

The foot is moving through pronation, and forces are at their peak, making this phase the most potentially injurious. Loads as high as two and a half times your body weight pushing down on unstable hip, knee, ankle and foot joints can wear down muscle, tissue and bone.

TOE-OFF

As you push off from the ground to propel yourself forwards, your hip goes into maximal extension. A major issue to consider during this phase of the running action is that if your hip flexors are too tight, you are more likely to excessively arch your back.

4 LEAD WITH YOUR HIPS

▨ **What it means**
Initiating the running motion from the centre of your body.
▨ **Why it matters**
Running from your hips and driving forward with your knees, not your feet, helps maintain a tall posture and avoid injury-inducing overstriding.
▨ **Try this**
Engage your core and imagine stepping over logs as you run. Focus on your foot landing close to your body, not out in front.

5 CHECK YOUR CADENCE

▨ **What it means**
The number of footfalls per minute.
▨ **Why it matters**
A faster cadence minimises overstriding and harmful forces on your joints.
▨ **Should you increase yours?**
Yes, if your easy stride rate is 160 steps per minute or less (a sign of overstriding) or if you're injury-prone. If you're above 160 and not injured or overstriding, upping your rate may not prevent injury, but could improve speed. Try increasing it by five per cent.

6 ENGAGE YOUR GLUTES

▨ **What it means**
Tapping your bum every now and then while you run is a simple way to remind your body to contract and engage your glute muscles as you run, says Dr Luke.
▨ **Why it matters**
It keeps you thinking about form. 'Having an awareness of what your body is doing, where your feet are and what muscles are working helps you become a better runner,' says Orton.

Photography **Studio 33**

THE RUNNER'S *MOT*

Check you're fit to run using these four self-tests, complete with fixes from top physiotherapists

Whether you're a running novice or veteran it's always a good idea to take a step back and assess whether or not your running body is as fit for purpose as you think. We asked leading physiotherapists to guide you through common niggles and problems that often inflict the recreational runner, and prescribe simple fixes that you can do at home. Each test should be performed on both legs. While you may feel a degree of discomfort with these moves – especially if it's an issue that causes you problems – if you experience acute pain with any of the tests, it's probably time to go and see an expert.

PROBLEM 1

TIGHT FEET AND CALVES

'Having weak feet manifests itself as tightness,' says Duncan Mason, a chartered physiotherapist at Athlete Matters in Worsley, Greater Manchester. The problems often stem from focusing exclusively on running and neglecting the conditioning side. Wearing very cushioned shoes is another cause, as thick midsole foam reduces the stresses that strengthen the feet. Also, Mason says feet and calves can be tight in forefoot/midfoot strikers or those trying to switch running style.

IF NOT TREATED...

Plantar fasciitis is when tight calf muscles result in a prolonged and significant pronation of the foot, leading to overstretching of the plantar fascia – a thick band of tissue that stretches from your heel to your midfoot bones.

TEST IT

A gentle upward stretch of the toes will tell you if your feet are tight: your plantar fascia will feel stiff and flexibility will be limited. To test for tight calves, sit in a chair and lift your leg straight out in front of you. Point your toes towards the ceiling and then pull back towards your knee, so you feel a stretch in the calves. You should be able to bend your ankle to 100 degrees. If you can't, you have tight calves.

FIX IT

'Single-leg calf raises [pictured] are a great way to improve functional strength of the calf and foot,' says Mason. 'Drop into a mini squat with your left knee flexed at 45 degrees. Do your max number of full calf raises, moving only at the right foot and ankle.' Continue until form is lost, then repeat on the other side. 'You should be able to do 30 reps a day,' says Mason.

PROBLEM 2

TIGHT HAMSTRINGS

We've all been there – 10 miles into a half marathon and an invisible vice clamps on to the back of your thighs. With every stride it strengthens its grip. 'The causes of tight hamstrings include overuse, a lack of flexibility or a limited range of motion emanating from 40-plus hours tapping away on a keyboard,' says Claire Callaghan, chartered physiotherapist at University of Bristol Sports Medicine Clinic.

IF NOT TREATED...

Because the hamstrings span the knee and hip joints, tightness can lead to pain in these areas and the lower back. Runners with tight hamstrings might notice they ride a bike with their knees splayed wide, which can make the situation worse.

TEST IT

'Lie down on your back,' says Callaghan. 'Pull your right thigh into your chest. Keep the thigh in the chest area and then extend your right knee, taking your foot toward the ceiling. The other leg remains straight on the floor. If your knee struggles to extend and you feel tightness or discomfort in the back of your upper left leg, your hamstrings are tight.'

FIX IT

A swift way to loosen hamstrings is to add dynamism to the self-diagnosis stretch. Do the exercise 10 times per day. 'You could also see a physio or running coach to check you're using your hip muscles correctly on the run,' says Callaghan.

'Small changes to ensure you're taking the weight on your standing leg correctly and extending your other leg can minimise tightness.'

PROBLEM 3

TIGHT QUADRICEPS

'One of the most common weaknesses for runners is in the quadriceps,' says Alison Rose, former physiotherapist to Kelly Holmes, Jess Ennis-Hill and the Brownlee brothers. 'It's caused by overuse, lack of proper stretching – especially post-exercise – and in general by our sedentary lifestyle.'

IF NOT TREATED...

Tight quads cause your pelvis to tilt forward, which puts stress on your lower back. Continue running down that path and you'll experience chronic back pain and tight hamstrings. 'If one quad is tighter than the other, it can cause a torsion in the pelvis, too,' adds Rose. That means one side of the hip is more rotated than the other, which can result in further back pain and painful buttocks.

TEST IT

Lying on your side with right arm bent, head rested on it, and right knee bent at a right angle, with your thigh level with your hips, pull your left leg by the ankle towards your bum with your left hand, (as shown). This is the muscle being length-tested, and it should be long enough to allow your thigh to be in line with your trunk and, ideally, with your heel touching your buttocks. If you're nowhere near reaching your bum with your heel, your quadricep muscles are too tight

FIX IT

To remedy the problem, you will need to hold the test stretch for three sets of 30 seconds, every day. You should repeat several times if you're extremely tight. 'Foam rolling the quads will also address this weakness,' explains Rose. 'It helps lengthen the quad and is also useful before stretching.'

PROBLEM 4

TIGHT HIPS

The hip provides the foundation for perfect running technique. It provides stability for the standing leg and boosts propulsion when you're looking for that extra gear. Typically, hip tightness is caused by our 21st-century lifestyle – in other words, too much sitting – repetitive use and weak glutes.

IF NOT TREATED...

'If there's a weakness or tightness in the hip area, it can lead to hip, lower back, iliotibial band and knee problems, too,' says David Barton, physiotherapist at Cobham and Weybridge Physiotherapy. 'These problems will be aggravated by an increase in mileage.' A weakness of the hips can also cause biomechanical issues like a pelvic tilt, which can cause bursitis. This is when a fluid-filled sac (bursa) on the outside of the top of the thigh bone becomes inflamed – often caused by repetitive movements of poor running technique.

TEST IT

There are a few tests to self-diagnose but one of the most accurate is the 'Thomas test', pictured left. 'Lie back on a table with less than half your thighs off the edge,' explains Barton. 'Bring both knees towards your chest, keep one there and extend the other leg back down. If the underside of that thigh is even slightly lifted off the table, it's a sign you're suffering from tight hip flexors.'

FIX IT

One of the best stretches for increasing hip flexibility is the hip flexor stretch. 'Kneel on the leg that you want to stretch,' says Barton. 'Then lunge forward with your other leg, while squeezing your glutes. Reach overhead towards the midline of your body with the arm on the same side as your kneeling leg. You should feel the stretch in the front of your hip and thigh. Hold the position for 30 seconds, relax and then repeat the move on the other side.'

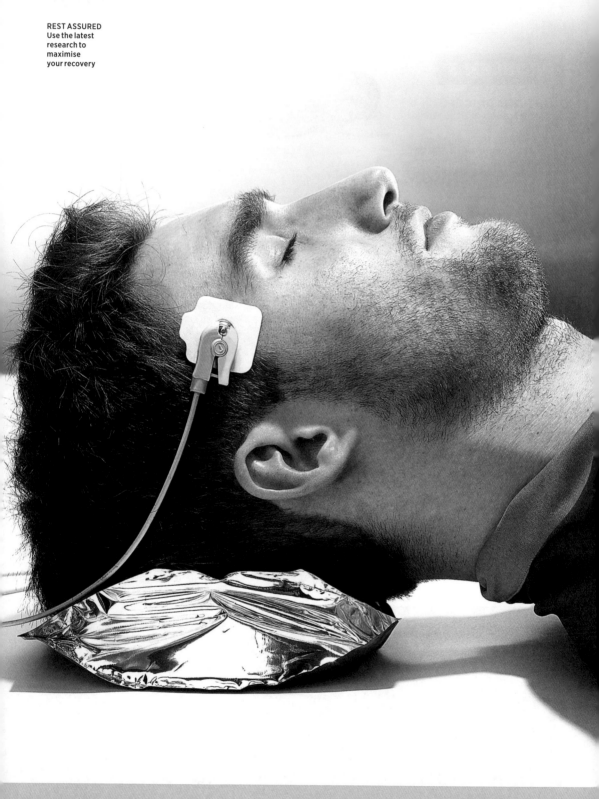

THE SCIENCE OF
RECOVERY

From milkshakes to massage, we put common recovery techniques under the microscope

Photography **Studio 33** Illustrations **Peter Liddiard**

Want to know the formula for running success? It goes: run, recover, repeat. While most of us get the beginning and end bits right, the middle step often gets overlooked. There are many reasons for this: mainly it's because as a nation we're time poor and can barely fit in the training let alone the recovery. However, we suspect there's also a belief that, unless you're running 80 miles a week or churning out sub-2:45 marathons, recovery doesn't really matter. The evidence certainly suggests that this is not the case. Sidestepping good recovery practice can leave you more susceptible to aches, pains, colds, infections, fatigue and injury – not to mention leaving you less than raring to go for your next session.

REST

Boost your performance by taking time out

One aspect of recovery you probably don't have too much of an issue with is the importance of rest. While running places stress on the body, triggering physiological adaptations, it's during rest that these adaptations actually take place. So if you don't get enough rest, you won't reap the benefits of all your hard training. But what does rest entail? Sitting on the sofa with your feet up? Sleeping?

Well, growth hormone – a substance that stimulates muscle growth and repair – is released while we sleep, aiding recovery and adaptation. Research at Bangor University in Wales found that even one night's sleep deprivation had a detrimental effect on running performance. But rest isn't all about getting your ZZZs in.

Researchers also found the rate of recovery from a tough treadmill run was significantly faster after practising the yoga pose savasana (meaning 'corpse pose') – the prostrate, upturned-palms position – compared with simply lying down. Yoga teacher and runner Laura Denham-Jones also recommends viparita karani, a pose in which you lie down and raise your legs (see Legs-Up-The-Wall Pose, on p135). 'Elevation helps relieve cramps and aids blood circulation to the upper body and head,' she says. 'The posture also provides a gentle stretch for the hamstrings and calves, and releases tension in the back.'

Even running itself can be a form of recovery: 'An easy run, bike ride or swim can be described as "active recovery',' explains Sarah Connors, a physiotherapist and member of the Asics Pro Team. 'The movement can help to flush toxins out of the working muscles, stimulate circulation and dissipate muscle tension and tightness.' If you opt for recovery running or cross-training, don't go push yourself too hard – keep the duration below 45 minutes and consider using a heart-rate monitor to ensure you are working at an easy pace. Also, stick to soft, even, surfaces such as dirt trails.

through a process called adaptive shortening, which will alter the function of the joints they attach to – not a good thing.

RECOVERY STRATEGY

Ideally, you should stretch your back and all the major lower body muscle groups after a run (see how, right). Hold each stretch for 20-30 seconds. Pushed for time? If you only have five minutes to spare, says Connors, focus on stretching the hip flexors, calves and hamstrings. 'Stretch out the hip flexors

lactic acid from muscles, sports massage actually slows down the process – by as much as 25 per cent. But, according to Lacey, the findings don't really downplay the importance of sports massage. 'It's not lactic acid that causes muscle soreness, it's microtrauma – the tiny tears in muscle fibres,' he says. 'And massage, through breaking down fibrous tissue and adhesions, can help heal the damage.'

A data review from Ohio State University in the US found moderate evidence to support the frequent use of massage therapy in assisting recovery – and evidence that it could help to alleviate the symptoms of delayed onset muscle soreness (DOMS).

There's also the psychological aspect of recovery to consider, says Lacey. 'You can do all your stretching and icing – but massage is something that's done for you. It makes you feel good because you are looking after yourself – it's a reward for all your hard training.' Even Michael Tschavosky, author of the Canadian study, says he's a fan of sports massage simply because it 'feels good'.

'The best way to go about finding a reputable therapist is simply by getting some good recommendations from other runners who you trust,' says Lacey. Or you can check out the Sports Massage Association website (sportsmassageassociation.org) to find a practitioner in your area.

FAIL TO STRETCH AND YOUR MUSCLES WILL STILL BE TIGHT NEXT TIME YOU RUN

RECOVERY STRATEGY

Build sufficient rest into your schedule – and that's not just taking rest days but also allowing recovery time after runs, before rushing on with your day. As an important race approaches, try to increase the amount of sleep you get to maximise the chances of a good performance.

first,' she advises. 'The more the hips release, the more the hamstrings will do the same.'

MASSAGE

Hands-on treatment will aid all-important muscular repair

Sports massage is widely used to help recovery and is part and parcel of every elite athlete's regime. 'Sports massage can release muscle tension, maintain flexibility and help to reduce the viscosity of intra-muscular fluid, which helps to flush out waste products,' explains Clive Lacey, sports massage therapist and lecturer (bodymaintenance.co.uk). 'If you have regular treatments, a good sports massage therapist should be able to spot any problem areas that, if left untreated, could end up turning into full-blown injuries further down the line.'

A study from Queen's University in Canada rubbed a few sports massage therapists up the wrong way by suggesting that far from aiding blood circulation and assisting in the removal of

STRETCHES

Neglect stretching and you can increase the risk of long-term damage

Most of us manage a few perfunctory post-run stretches, but are we doing enough to aid recovery? 'Running causes the muscles to contract repeatedly so the fibres end up tight and sometimes misaligned, like hair that needs combing,' says Connors. 'If you don't help restore them to their resting length, the next time you run they will still be tight. This could have a knock-on effect on your risk of injury.' Over time and in the absence of stretching, muscle fibres can permanently lose length

RECOVERY STRATEGY

If your budget can stretch to it, book yourself in for regular treatments when training – once a month, or more, is ideal. Otherwise, schedule massage for a couple of days after a long run. The rest of the time, you can top up with self-massage techniques.

'Work from foot to hip, using the flat or heel of the hand, fingers or thumbs,' says Lacey. 'When you find a tight area, massage gently for a few minutes and then apply light to

RECOVERY **STRETCHES**

Spend at least 30 seconds on each of these after a run, to enhance performance and reduce your risk of injury

CALVES
How to ease these lower leg muscles

Take a big step forwards with your right foot, bending the knee. Keep the left leg straight and have both sets of toes pointing directly forwards **(1)**. Now gently press your heel down into the ground. Keep your torso upright and back straight. Now take a half-step forward with your left leg and bend both knees, keeping the left heel on the floor to feel the stretch in the lower part of the calf **(2)**. Finally, take the left foot directly behind the right and place the ball of the left foot up against the heel of the right foot, so that the toes are pointing upwards **(3)**. This stretches the plantar fascia under the foot. Repeat these stretches on the other side.

LEGS-UP-THE-WALL POSE
Boost your circulation

Sit sideways with your right hip flush to the wall. With one smooth movement **(1)**, breathe out, swing your legs up the wall and lower your head and torso to the floor **(2)**. Shimmy your hips towards the wall – if your hamstrings are tight you'll need to scoot back, and if your feet splay apart, tie your legs together with a scarf. You can also place a folded blanket or towel under the hips, with the top edge below your ribs, for a passive backbend. Bring your arms to a comfortable position by your sides. Relax your legs, shoulders and belly, and focus on breathing freely. You can hold this position for anything up to 15 minutes.

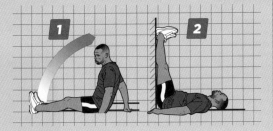

LEG RELEASE
Give your calves, hamstrings and quads some TLC

Sit on the floor with your knees bent. With your hands either side of your left leg, hook your fingers behind the knee and repeatedly draw the foot towards the buttocks in long, smooth strokes **(1)**. Swap legs and repeat the motion. Then drop your knees out to each side then draw them together **(2)**. Repeat, slowly building up momentum until you get a rhythm.

HIP FLEXORS
If you're in a rush, this is the most crucial stretch

Take a big step forwards with your left foot, bending the knee and allowing your right knee to rest on the floor, as shown. Bring your torso upright and curl your tailbone under – then gently press your right hip forwards. Swap sides and repeat.

HAMSTRINGS
A simple move to loosen your upper leg muscles

Stand in front of a step that's mid-shin to mid-thigh height and place your right foot on its surface, with the leg straight **(1)**. Your support leg should be vertical, with the foot facing forward. Now hinge forward from the hips until you feel a stretch along the back of the thigh **(2)**. Don't curve your back. If your hamstrings are tight, repeat the stretch with the leg pointing to one o'clock position, and then pointing to 11 o'clock.

medium pressure, holding for up to seven seconds before gently stretching out that area. Using one hand on top of the other allows you to apply more force. Avoid rubbing bony areas and stay away from sites of injury – incorrect treatment could make problems worse.'

ICE

Reduce inflammation and increase blood flow

Running causes lots of tiny tears in the muscles and tendons – and lowering body temperature shunts blood away from the area, reducing inflammation. But science suggests you don't need to plunge yourself into an ice bath, like some elites do. 'As long as it's cold enough to reduce your body temperature, it'll do fine,' says Connors. Recent research found immersion into 10°C water after all-out exercise did not improve later performance, but subjects did report they felt better, and a study published in the *International Journal of Sports Medicine* found that cold-water immersion and contrast therapy (alternating between hot and cold water) aided recovery from repeated hard efforts, while complete rest and hot-water immersion did not. Also, research from New Zealand found 'cool' to 'body temperature' water may provide the best recovery, citing the benefits of increased blood flow, transportation of nutrients and removal of waste products.

RECOVERY STRATEGY

Hold the shower nozzle over your leg muscles, gradually reducing the water temperature. Or, if you're a hardier soul, for the lower legs, a bucket full of cold water works a treat on sore Achilles and plantar fascias. Ice is good for specific injuries, but not necessary for general recovery.

THE COOLDOWN

Don't underestimate the effects of slowing down gradually after a run

When you run, the blood vessels in your legs dilate to accommodate the increased blood flow. That's why, if you stop too suddenly, you can cause blood to pool in the legs, leaving you feeling dizzy or shaky. Coming to a more gradual stop helps prevent this, but there's no evidence that it will reduce muscle soreness afterwards. In one South African study, subjects were assigned a workout to instigate sore leg muscles. Some did a cool-down (walking slowly for 10 minutes) while others simply stopped. There was no difference in levels of reported muscle soreness. That said, a cool-down marks the transition between running and getting back to your day. A US study found that cooling-down enhanced the overall exercise experience by allowing you time to take stock of and reflect upon your achievements.

RECOVERY STRATEGY

If you've been running at a faster pace or for a prolonged period, take a few minutes at the end of the run to slow down gradually, allowing your heart rate and breathing frequency to return to normal.

COMPRESSION GEAR

Use compression tights post-run to reduce aches and pains

The fact that a recent study by Indiana University, US, concluded that compression clothing had no significant effect on athletic performance hasn't stopped many a runner donning full-length tights or knee-high socks. And the good news is that science is proving to be a little more promising on the benefits of the big squeeze on recovery. In other words, donning compression gear after exercise rather than during it. Research published in the *Journal of Sports Science and Medicine* found that graduated compression tights (where the compression is greatest at the ankle and diminishes further up the leg) hastened recovery after a period of downhill walking by allowing faster cell repair.

Vanessa Davies, the physiologist who conducted the study, found reduced levels of creatine kinase (an enzyme that indicates muscle damage), 24 and 48 hours after subjects performed repeated jumps from a height, when they recovered in compression tights.

In other research from Ball State University, US, use of compression gear following maximal exercise prevented loss of range of motion, reduced swelling and promoted the recovery of force production. Davies' study subjects, in common with those from the Ball State University study, reported that they felt that putting on compression tights helped reduce muscle soreness. 'The psychological element could be as strong a factor as the physical,' says Davies.

RECOVERY STRATEGY

After a shower and stretch, slip (OK, squeeze) on a pair of compression tights or socks. You can even put them on under your jeans thanks to the tight fit, and no one will be any the wiser. Some athletes even sleep in them.

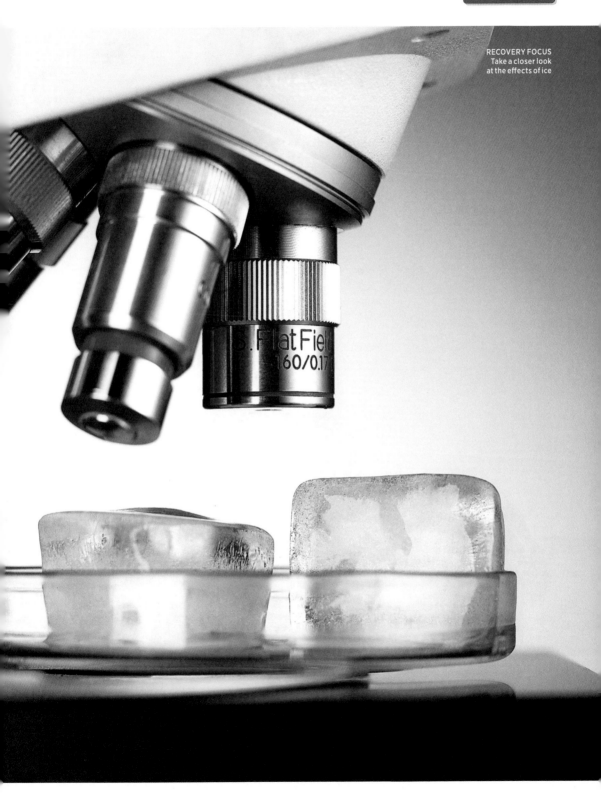

RECOVERY FOCUS
Take a closer look
at the effects of ice

s. Flat Fiel
60/0.17

**THE GRASS
IS GREENER**
Go off road now
and again to
save your legs

SOFT
LANDING

Run on trails, grass, sand or even in water to reduce your injury risk and boost your performance

Most runners log their miles on the streets, but roads shouldn't be your only training ground. 'Running on different surfaces changes the scenery, workout and effort, giving road runners a break,' says running coach Jennifer Novak. Running once or twice a week on grass, sand, trails – or even in a pool – reduces the impact on your legs, which minimises injury risk. And pushing off on softer surfaces strengthens more muscles, which can translate into faster times on the road. Here's how to adapt your workout to whatever lies beneath.

GRASS

Running on grass produces up to 17 per cent less pressure on your feet than running on roads, says a recent study in the *Journal of Sports Sciences*. This makes it ideal for runners on the mend who want a forgiving surface to help them transition back to the streets. It's also ideal for runners looking to minimise injury risk while increasing mileage or intensity.

What to do there: Speedwork
On a neat, level surface, such as a football pitch, warm up and then run three minutes, two minutes and one minute hard, with a one-minute rest in-between. The intensity should be such that you can speak just a word or two at a time. Start with two to three sets and progress to five.

SAND

The unstable surface of a beach helps strengthen muscles in your feet, legs, hips and core, says Novak. Sand running also ramps up the aerobic challenge, burning about 1.6 times more calories than road running, reports the *Journal of Experimental Biology*. But avoid sand if you're returning from injury, since it puts extra strain on your lower legs and calves, says Novak.

What to do there: Easy runs
Begin sand running by finishing your road workout with five easy minutes; stay on the harder sand, close to the water, for more traction, says Novak. Progress to seven minutes easy, running reps of two minutes on the hard sand and 20 seconds on softer sand.

TRAILS

Hitting the trail keeps your mind on movement. 'The rocks, trees, roots and turns require focus if you're to be safe,' says Novak. As well as giving your brain a workout regularly shifting gears and adjusting to terrain also puts your leg muscles through a varied range of movements.

What to do there: Hills
Find a trail with inclines of a low and moderate grade. Run at a conversational pace for half to two-thirds the distance of your average easy run. 'On each ascent, lean forward, keep your arms pumping, use short strides and land on the centre of your foot,' says running coach Robert Rhodes. 'Most importantly, breathe,' Each week, pick up the pace until you're running uphill comfortably hard – an eight on a scale of one to 10.

WATER

Striding through water isn't just rehab for injured runners – it's also useful if you want to build strength. 'Water offers continuous resistance,' says Michael J Ryan, assistant professor of exercise science at Fairmont State University, US. Your muscles have to push at every point of your stride; on land they get a breather when they're airborne.

What to do there: Intervals
First of all find a quiet pool. After warming up in chest- to shoulder-deep water, do the following: two to three minutes hard, 30 seconds all out, then three minutes jogging. Repeat three times and add one set every two weeks. Moving to shallower water (waist-deep or lower) will increase the impact and work your lower leg muscles even harder, says Ryan.

Photography **Mathew Scott**

PILLOW
TALK

Getting more quality sleep can make you
a stronger, better runner – here's how

Photography **Studio 33**

SHEEP DREAMS
Running success
starts between
the sheets

Being honest, many runners would probably admire the hardy soul who fights through fatigue to get out of bed and complete a run. Likewise, many would consider the runner who wakes tired and decides to sleep in rather than grind out a workout a bit of a slacker.

Modern society views sleep as a luxury, and many people think that revealing your need for it marks you out as a weakling, says Dr John Caldwell, a psychologist who has researched sleep deprivation and fatigue for NASA. 'We think if you're really a good athlete, that means you're tough and you'll

important as your workouts,' says running coach Joe English. 'When you start robbing from that pot to get everything else done, the quality of your training – and of everything else – starts to fall apart.'

ARE YOU GETTING ENOUGH?

No test can tell you exactly how many hours of sleep you need, but the average adult needs between seven and nine hours a night, says Dr Matthew Edlund, author of *The Power of Rest* (HarperOne). Not surprisingly, how much you run impacts on how much you need to sleep, but it's not a simple

> DURING SLEEP YOUR BODY RECOVERS AND BUILDS YOU INTO A BETTER RUNNER

take whatever life throws your way,' he says. Part of being tough is not needing to sleep, seems to be the thinking.

By that line of reasoning, the world's top marathoners are total slouches. Post-run naps are a key feature in the elite Kenyan training day, the American 2:04 marathoner Ryan Hall notes naps in his calendar as 'business meetings', while Paula Radcliffe's world dominance was fuelled by 10 hours' sleep a night – topped up with a two-hour afternoon nap. They clearly appreciate what science is increasingly revealing: it's during sleep that your body recovers from hard training and builds you into a better runner.

Indeed, recent research suggests that just one night of bad rest can have a negative impact on your running performance. Meanwhile, chronically denying yourself an hour of sleep each night has cumulative negative effects on your running and your health. 'Sleep is as

more-means-more equation. Research has linked moderate exercise to higher-quality, more efficient slumber – possibly by increasing levels of the sleep-promoting compound adenosine. So, people logging moderate mileage might actually need less sleep than those who don't do any running at all.

However, sleep needs can change in the middle of a tough training cycle, says Cheri Mah, a sleep researcher at Stanford University in the US. There's no chart for correlating mileage to required sleep hours, but your body should supply some cues when you don't get enough. You're probably short on decent rest if you fall asleep the second your

SLEEP CYCLE

At night you'll go through four stages of sleep,

N1
Very light sleep (about five per cent of your night): this occurs when you first fall asleep and again after each interruption. Your brain waves shift and your muscles relax.

N2
Light sleep (about 50 per cent of your night): your breathing and heart rate relax. It's more difficult to wake up if your sleep is disturbed.

NAP **TIME?**

A terrible night's sleep and a workout planned later? Is a siesta a good idea?

YES
If you can limit your snooze to less than 30 minutes. A short nap can give you a cognitive boost, making you feel alert and motivated. And that can translate to a better run. You don't even need to fall asleep; just resting quietly for a few minutes can be restorative.

NO
If you're having regular problems sleeping at night. Napping can make it difficult to drift off later – and it's no substitute for a complete night of rest. Also, you may wake up after a longer nap feeling groggier than you did before you snoozed.

head hits the pillow, doze off during meetings, rely on caffeine to get through the day or hit the snooze button more than once. 'If your body is going back to sleep after being asleep all night, you're probably not getting enough,' says Dr Robert Oexman, a runner and the director of the Sleep to Live Institute in North Carolina, US.

Ignore these signals at your peril. 'When you don't get your required amount of sleep, it can build up like a debt or a credit card,' says Mah. 'Over time, that accumulated debt can affect performance and mood.'

WHILE YOU WERE DREAMING...
Night after night of restricted (or interrupted) sleep sets off a cascade of hormonal shifts with harmful biological effects. Within a week or two, you'll have higher levels of the inflammatory marker C-reactive protein and the stress hormone cortisol, keeping your heart rate higher and your nervous system on constant alert.

Human growth hormone, which repairs muscle and bones, is secreted by your pituitary gland during deep sleep, says Shelby Harris, director of the Behavioral Sleep Medicine Programme at Montefiore Medical Center in New York. The less sleep you get, the lower your levels. Your muscles' ability to store glycogen for energy also declines, meaning you risk running out of gas no matter how much you carb-load, says Harris. Plus, there's some research that indicates your injury risk goes up if you don't get enough shut-eye.

Sleep also serves as a time for memory consolidation, says Dr Edlund. 'Running is a very big learning experience,' he says. As you train, your brain takes in information about the world around you, the way muscles and nerves must work together to power each stride, and the way your

which make up a full sleep cycle that lasts 90-110 minutes.

N3
Deep sleep (about 20 per cent of your night); the most restorative rest; your body secretes human growth hormone and it's nearly impossible to wake up.

REM
Rapid eye movement sleep (about 25 per cent of your night): your eyes, face, arms and legs twitch, and your brainwaves speed up again. Most dreams occur during this stage.

body position shifts in space (proprioception), he explains. It's during sleep you process, synthesise and catalogue these details, and skimping means the memory-related areas of your brain don't file away as much as they should.

Being sleep deprived doesn't just make you tired, but also jittery, achy and prone to injury. There's no magic number of hours that protects you from poor performance or from running-related pains – again, everyone's sleep needs differ, says Dr Edlund. But the more nights you get less than your required amount, the greater the potential consequences to your running. And in the bigger picture, you're probably

Research supports this hypothesis, to a degree. When scientists keep people up all night and then ask them to cycle, lift weights or run on a treadmill, they can generally do it just as well as when they've slept. But, interestingly, they report that each mile or rep feels harder and they often don't want to put in the effort. 'In order to run a good race, you have to be in a state of mind where you're going to push it,' says Caldwell. 'We've known for years that sleep deprivation typically doesn't really affect absolute things like muscle contractions, speed and power. But it definitely affects your willingness to perform at your best.'

SCHEDULE YOUR BEDTIME IN ADVANCE, AS YOU WOULD ANY OTHER COMMITMENT

harming your overall health, too. Sleep deprivation throws your hunger hormones out of whack, increasing levels of hunger-inducing ghrelin and decreasing satiating leptin, says Harris, which may cause you to gain weight. Not getting enough sleep also suppresses the immune system, negatively affects mood and ups the risk of developing chronic diseases such as type 2 diabetes.

CRASH AND BURN

Runners know insomnia is common the night before a big race. But they take comfort from this oft-dispensed piece of wisdom: 'It's not your sleep the night before a race – it's the night before the night before that counts.' Anecdotal evidence bears this out. No one sleeps much the night before an Olympic race, says Paula Schnurr, who ran the 1500m for Canada at the 1996 Games. First-time marathoners often don't rest well either, but many perform strongly anyway, fuelled by race-day excitement and adrenaline.

When you head out for a training run deprived of sleep and with no cheering crowds or competition, these deficits could lead you to slack off. As a result, you might not give your body a strong enough stimulus to adapt and improve your running, says English. What's more, lack of sleep impairs cognitive function and reaction times, which could put you at risk of a collision if you're crossing busy roads, warns neurologist Dr Lev Grinman.

In fact, if you've slept fewer than six hours, you might benefit more from staying in bed an hour longer than from forcing yourself to stumble out on a run, says Dr Shawn Youngstedt, an exercise physiology researcher at the University of South Carolina, US. Many people can bounce back quickly from one or two nights of poor rest, but performing well gets harder the longer you're deprived.

When Mah asked case-study athletes from various sports to sleep for 10 hours a night for five to seven weeks, they

improved their performance. Now, spending almost half the day in bed isn't a luxury most of us can afford, but it may not even be necessary. Your body's optimal amount could be seven hours; it could be eight. Harris recommends determining your ideal sleep pattern when you have a week's holiday or at another time that doesn't require a strict schedule; don't use an alarm clock, wake up naturally and take note of what time you went to sleep and got up. By the fourth day, you'll have caught up on sleep debt; take the average amount of sleep you get on nights four to seven for a good estimate of your true needs, she says. Once you've worked out how much sleep your body naturally wants, schedule your bedtime in advance, just like you would any other commitment, Caldwell advises.

Mah says that runners can still benefit from 'sleep-loading' – getting extra shut-eye in the week or two before beginning a

BEST OF THE *REST*

Fall - and stay - fast asleep with these expert tips

BE CONSISTENT
Stick to the same sleep/wake schedule. And create a relaxing pre-sleep ritual, such as doing light yoga or listening to calming music. Adopting a bedtime routine will prompt your body to fall asleep more easily, says sleep researcher Cheri Mah.

HIBERNATE
'Make your room like a cave – dark, quiet and cool,' says Mah. Invest in blackout curtains and a white-noise machine or fan, and block glowing lights from alarm clocks or phones.

POWER DOWN
Turn off TVs, laptops and tablets an hour before bedtime – their light blocks the production of the sleep hormone melatonin, says Shelby Harris, director of Montefiore's Behavioral Sleep Medicine Program in New York.

DRINK LESS
To avoid middle-of-the-night loo stumbles, cut back on water consumption three hours before bedtime, Harris says. Beer or wine may help you conk out more quickly, but alcohol disrupts the later, deeper stages of sleep.

CUT OFF CAFFEINE
It can linger in your system for more than six hours. For best results, switch to decaf (or at least green tea, which contains only about 50 milligrams of caffeine) after 5pm, says sleep researcher Dr Christopher Drake.

EASE PAIN NATURALLY
Anti-inflammatories such as ibuprofen keep some people up at night. Avoid taking them before bed or try a supplement such as fish oil or glucosamine chondroitin instead, says Dr Oexman.

training programme that ramps up your mileage. Committing to just half an hour more each night to pay off your sleep debt between training cycles enables you to kick off a new programme refreshed and strong. 'That's half an hour less checking your email,' says Mah. And it's likely you'll feel so good during this period that you'll make an earlier bedtime a permanent policy.

ENERGY CRISIS
Many experts also recommend tracking your sleep – just as you log your miles – to help you correlate your rest to your running performance. Invest in an activity monitor (such as the Fitbit One Wireless Activity and Sleep Tracker, fitbit.com) – these devices track your daily activity and monitor how long and how well you sleep at night. They come with apps and online dashboards to show you your snoozing stats.

While that won't give you more hours in the day, it may help you place sleep and training on an equal footing. 'If you're obsessed with logging your 40 miles, try to be as obsessed with logging your hours of sleep a week,' says English. 'It's going to positively impact on the quality of your workouts.'

Keeping track can also help you recognise if something goes awry in your training. In a study published in the journal *Medicine & Science in Sports & Exercise*, athletes who overreached – or who ran more miles or did more intense workouts than their bodies could handle – showed disrupted sleep patterns. If you're unable to sleep well, it could mean you need to cut back or incorporate more rest days to absorb the hard work you're doing, says study author Dr Yann LeMeur, from the National Institute for Sport, Expertise, and Performance in Paris.

Finally, monitoring your sleep habits often gives you a bigger-picture view of whether your goals mesh with your life at the moment, says Harris. If you've just had a baby, for instance, now may not be the time to train for your first marathon. 'You have to be realistic – maybe you just can't get up at five in the morning to run if you can't get to bed until midnight,' says Harris. You don't have to stop running – just consider whether you should scale back expectations or run for stress relief rather than trying to stick to an aggressive plan. On the flipside, if you have an ambitious running goal, plan it for a time when you can rearrange your life to accommodate the necessary training and recovery.

And if you happen to be updating Facebook, you should feel as proud to post about getting a good night's sleep as about getting your miles in. As the 2:04 marathoner Ryan Hall says, if you cannot recover from your training, then there is no point training.

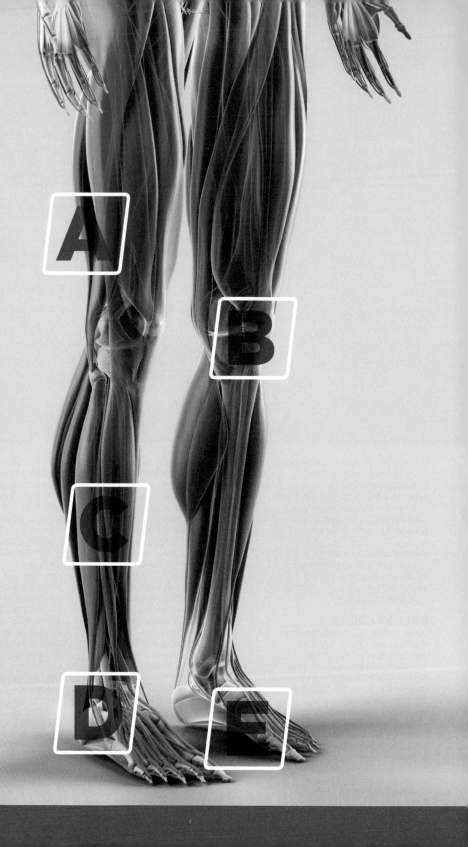

INJURY
CLINIC

If you suffer any of the five common injuries
below, don't worry: our experts can fix you

CONTENTS

A **ITB SYNDROME**

B **RUNNER'S KNEE**

C **SHIN SPLINTS**

D **ACHILLES TENDONITIS**

E **PLANTAR FASCIITIS**

Photography **Getty** Illustrations **Anne Cakebread and Elite Fitness (Cardiff)**

A ILIOTIBIAL BAND SYNDROME

PAIN, EXPLAINED

Leading sports performance specialist Dr Carlyle Jenkins explains why your knee feels like it's got a stake driven through it.

1 ILIOTIBIAL BAND

Your iliotibial band (ITB) is a ligament-like structure that starts at your pelvis and runs along the outside of your thigh to the outside of the top of your shin bone (tibia). When you run, your ITB rubs back and forth over a bony outcrop on your knee, which helps to stabilise it.

2 LATERAL EPICONDYLE

If you have poor running mechanics, muscle imbalance, increase your body weight or add hill running to your training, then your ITB can track out of line, slipping out of the groove created by this bony outcrop .

3 SWELLING

As it tracks out of its natural alignment it rubs against other structures in your leg, creating friction on the band. This results in inflammation and a click when you bend your knee.

4 HOLD-UP

The scarring thickens and tightens the ITB, and limits the blood flow. If you continue to run, you'll feel a stinging sensation. This can result in you limping soon after you have finished a run.

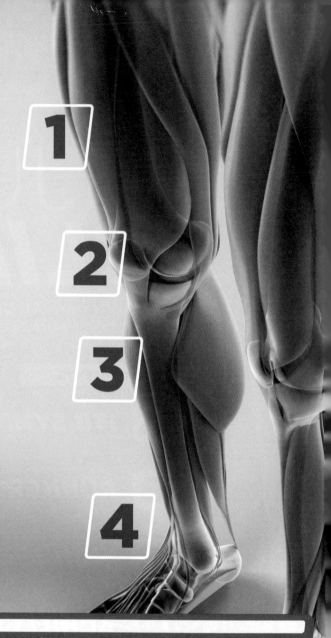

CAUSE & EFFECT

Why it happens and how you are able to spot it

WHAT CAUSES IT?

According to research in the *Clinical Journal of Sports Medicine*, these are the roots of the problem:

■ Inadequate warm-up
■ Increasing distance, speed or excessive downhill running
■ High or low arches can cause your feet to overpronate
■ Uneven leg length
■ Bow legs
■ Excessive wear on the outside heel of your trainers
■ Weak hip abductors
■ Running on a banked surface.

SPOT IT!

According to Dr Jenkins, you're a likely ITB sufferer if you experience one of the following signs:

■ A sharp or burning pain on the outside of the knee. This may subside shortly after running, but returns with the next run.
■ Tenderness on the outside of your knee if you apply pressure, especially when bending.
■ Issues standing on one leg (affected side), due to a weak gluteus medius.

HOW TO REHABILITATE IT

Decrease your training load by 50 per cent and apply the principles of RICE (rest, ice, compression and elevation), then use these tips.

DONKEY KICKS
- On all fours, rest on your knees and flatten your elbows on the floor so you're in a Sphinx-like position.
- Keep your head down and your right knee bent as you slowly lift your right leg up behind you so your foot rises up towards the ceiling.
- Hold that position for one second, then slowly return to the start. Perform four sets of 12 repetitions on each leg.

WHY?
This move hits and strengthens your gluteus maximus and medius. Research in the journal *Physical Therapy in Sport* has found that these muscles are vital for keeping your ITB strong and injury-free.

LYING ITB STRETCH
- Sit on the edge of a bench or firm bed. Lie back and pull the unaffected leg to your chest to flatten your lower back.
- With your affected leg flat to the bench, maintain a 90-degree bend in its knee. Shift that knee as far inwards to the side as possible.
- Hold this position for 30 seconds and repeat four times on each leg. Increase time if it feels too easy.

WHY?
'The ITB is difficult to elongate, as it doesn't have nerves that allow you to feel if you're actually stretching it. You might not feel this move in the ITB, but it does isolate the band,' says Jenkins.

SIDE CLAMSHELL
- Lie on a mat on your side, bending knees and hips to a 90 degree angle. Wrap a resistance band around both of your thighs.
- With the resistance band in place lift your top knee up towards the ceiling, making sure that the insides of both feet stay together.
- Perform 10-15 reps, or continue until you get a burn in the outside of your hip, which indicates you should stop.

WHY?
This move works your gluteus medius (on the outer surface of the pelvis). This muscle prevents your thigh from buckling inwards when you run, which is the root of ITB aches and pains.

HOW LONG UNTIL YOU'RE RECOVERED?
According to Jenkins, these are the recovery rates of iliotibial band syndrome, depending on the severity of your injury.

MILD INJURY	100% AFTER 2-4 WEEKS
AVERAGE INJURY	100% AFTER 7-8 WEEKS
SEVERE INJURY	100% AFTER 9-24 WEEKS

B | RUNNER'S KNEE

PAIN, EXPLAINED
Dr Ross Sherman, senior exercise physiologist and sports science consultant at Kingston University, London, explains what causes it.

1 QUADS
The thigh muscles above the knee hold your kneecap in place. When you run, your kneecap moves up and down your thigh bone (femur) without touching it.

2 KNEECAP
If your quads are weak or you have poor foot mechanics, your kneecap will move left and right, creating pressure, friction and irritation. As you clock up the miles and stride out your misaligned steps, your kneecap rubs against the end of your thighbone.

3 CARTILAGE
This wobbling and rubbing grinds down the cartilage underneath your kneecap so that it becomes rough, like sandpaper. This makes your knee unable to bend smoothly and efficiently.

4 FRONT KNEE PAIN
When this happens, you will experience a dull, aching pain under or around the front of your kneecap. The pinch will be the worst when running down a hill, walking down stairs, squatting down or sitting with a bent knee.

CAUSE & EFFECT
Why it happens and how you are able to spot it

WHAT CAUSES IT?
According to research in the *Journal of Sports Medicine*, these are the main culprits:

- Weak quadriceps
- Overuse or an increase in mileage
- Knock knees
- Tight hamstrings or calves
- A previous injury, such as a dislocation of the kneecap
- Overpronation or supination
- Uneven surfaces

SPOT IT!
Your doctor will give you the Clarke's Test (a component of knee examination) but you can do it yourself:

- Sit with your leg stretched out on another chair in front of you. Tense your quadricep.
- Gently squeeze above the knee with your right hand and push on the outside of the kneecap with your left hand.
- Feel a twinge? Then it's runner's knee.

'If a pain radiates into your back, hips and feet when you do this, then see a physiotherapist, who can examine you correctly and determine the root of the problem,' says Richard Scrivener, a running and injury lecturer at Premier Training.

HOW TO REHABILITATE IT

After applying the rules of RICE, rest from all sports for one to two weeks. Then perform these moves from Sherman two to three times a week.

LYING LEG LIFTS
- Lie flat on your back. Bend your left knee at 90 degrees, keeping your foot flat on floor.
- Keep your right leg perfectly straight and lift it to the height of the left knee.
- Hold for five to 10 seconds and repeat five to 10 times on both legs.

WHY?
'When out running on the road or track, your body weight lands on a near-straightened knee,' says Sherman. 'This move strengthens your quads – the muscle that absorbs the blow – in the position they receive the impact. This stabilises the injured knee.'

BALL HALF SQUATS
- Put a Swiss ball between you – on your lower back – and a stable wall.
- Lower yourself towards the floor. Stop when your knees are bent at 90 degrees.
- Straighten your legs to rise to the top without locking your knees.

WHY?
'You should do four to five sets of these, with 12 repetitions to strengthen your quads, lower back, glutes and core area. These muscle groups all work together to teach your knees to start bending correctly through their natural range of movement,' advises Sherman.

FOOT TURNS
- Stretch both legs out straight in front of you, feet pointed up.
- Turn both feet out away from each other as far as possible. Hold for 12 seconds while tensing your quads.
- Then turn them in towards each other for 12 seconds. That's one set; perform six.

WHY?
'The idea of this is to strengthen both your outer and inner quadricep muscles. This will then, in turn, strengthen and develop the cartilage that surrounds either side of the kneecap, which will stop it from tracking out of line in future,' says Sherman.

HOW LONG UNTIL YOU'RE RECOVERED?

According to Sherman, recovery rates depend on the severity of the injury. If it's mild, you rest for two weeks and do the rehab exercises you can be recovered in six weeks. If severe, it could take up to six months.

MILD INJURY
40-50% BETTER AFTER 1-2 WEEKS
60-75% BETTER AFTER A MONTH
100% BETTER AFTER 6-8 WEEKS

SEVERE INJURY
30-40% BETTER AFTER 2-3 WEEKS
50-60% BETTER AFTER 2 MONTHS
100% BETTER AFTER 4-6 MONTHS

SHIN SPLINTS

PAIN, EXPLAINED
Dr Carlyle Jenkins explains the reasons for that persistent ache in your shins.

1 TIBIALIS ANTERIOR
Shin splints are an overuse injury. The muscle most affected by this is the tibialis anterior, stretching from your knee down to your ankle. A new or excessive stress from running can irritate it.

2 TIBIA
By resting and applying our rehab tips when you feel mild tenderness in your shin bone (tibia), you'll eliminate further damage. But if you soldier on with more miles, then you'll create micro-tears.

3 OUTER SHIN PAIN
This is when you'll feel a razor-sharp pain on the outer edges of the mid region of your lower leg, next to the shin bone. The aching area can measure 10-15 centimetres, and the pain often subsides after warming up, returning after the workout.

4 REST UP
Worst-case scenario is that the swelling in the muscle and surrounding connective tissue continues unabated, increasing the pressure to intolerable levels. This can lead to 'Compartment Syndrome', a condition that can require surgery.

CAUSE & **EFFECT**
Why it happens and how you are able to spot it

WHAT CAUSES IT?
The Mayo Clinic in the US found that shin splints are caused by an overload on the shin bone and connective tissues, which attach your muscles to the bone. This overload is often caused by:

- Running downhill
- Running on a slanted or tilted surface
- Running in worn-out footwear
- Doing sports with frequent starts and stops, such as tennis
- Shin splints can also be caused by training too hard, too fast or for too long
- Overpronation; the tibia is forced to twist in the opposite direction. Too much leads to shin splints
- A return to exercise after a long layoff

SPOT IT!
The Mayo Clinic found that there are several telltale signs of shin splints, which are:

- Tenderness, soreness or pain running along the outer part of your lower leg.
- Mild swelling of the muscles around your shin bone.
- At first, the pain may end when you've finished your warm-up. Eventually, however, the pain may be continuous.

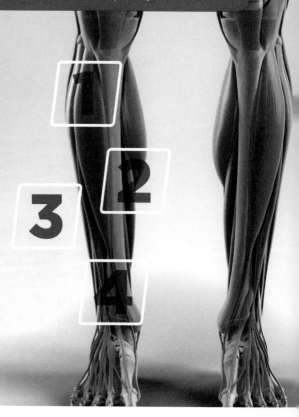

HOW TO REHABILITATE IT

Decrease your training load by 90-95 per cent and use RICE then do these rehabilitation moves from Dr Carlyle Jenkins once a day.

KNEELING STRETCH
- Get into a kneeling position, with your toes tucked under your backside, sitting on the back of your ankles.
- Lean forward towards the floor, spread out your fingers and rest them on the ground in front of you.
- Gently sit back onto your heels so that your ankles almost flatten against the floor. Hold for 30 seconds and repeat as needed.

WHY?
'This move will stretch out the muscles and connective tissue that is in the front of your legs and will alleviate some of the pressure in the painful part of your shin,' says Jenkins.

SEATED STRETCH
- Sit on a chair with your feet roughly hip-width apart on the floor, and place your hands on your knees.
- Bend your right leg behind you underneath the chair and rest the top part of your foot on the floor.
- Push your foot into the floor and press down on your right knee with your right hand. Hold for 30 seconds, switch legs and repeat.

WHY?
'This move is very efficient at isolating and loosening your shin muscles,' says Jenkins. 'It can also be easily done several times during the day while you are sitting at your desk at work.'

STANDING STRETCH
- Stand in front of a wall, roughly arm's length away, with your feet approximately hip-width apart.
- Lean forwards and place your hands on the wall while keeping both your feet forwards and knees straight.
- Lean as far forwards as possible while keeping your feet flat. Stop leaning when you feel an intense stretch and hold for 30 seconds.

WHY?
This move stretches the muscles at the back of your calves while resetting the muscles in your lower leg to the correct position to allow healing to commence effectively.

HOW LONG UNTIL YOU'RE RECOVERED?
An online poll on the fitness website attackpoint.org found that these were the expected recovery rates for shin splints.

MILD INJURY	100% AFTER 1-2 WEEKS
AVERAGE INJURY	100% AFTER 7-8 WEEKS
SEVERE INJURY	100% AFTER 9-24 WEEKS

D

ACHILLES TENDONITIS

Dr Carlyle Jenkins explains why your Achilles heel may be aching.

1 ACHILLES TENDON
This connects the calf muscles to the heel bone. It's the thick, springy tissue just above the heel and is used when you walk, run, jump or push up on your toes. Injury can occur if you up your training frequency or intensity.

2 FEEL THE BURN
Achilles tendonitis is a 'chronic stress' injury where small stresses accumulate and damage the tendon. This strain is increased if you're inflexible or you overpronate.

3 HEEL
The inflammation is often at the narrow point of the tendon, just above the heel area. This is because that area has the poorest blood supply, which slows the healing time considerably. Rest to avoid further pain.

4 ANKLE
You'll feel an ache at the back of your ankle and a burning or piercing pain. You'll experience redness on the tendon and/or severe pain when you take your first steps of the morning or after sitting down for a while. This will subside as you move around.

1

2

CAUSE & **EFFECT**
Why it happens and how you are able to spot it

WHAT CAUSES IT?
According to the American Academy of Orthopaedic Surgeons, these are the triggers:

- Rapidly increasing mileage or speed
- Adding hill running to your routine
- Starting too quickly after a layoff

- Trauma caused by sudden contraction of your calf muscles, such as intervals or a final sprint
- Overuse resulting from a lack of flexibility in your calf muscles
- Flattening of the arch of your foot can place stress on your Achilles

SPOT IT!
Research at the Mayo Clinic, US, found that it's likely you have Achilles tendonitis if you suffer with one or more of these symptoms:

- Dull ache or pain on the tendon when pushing off your foot during walking or

when rising onto your toes.
- Tenderness of your Achilles tendon.
- Stiffness that lessens as your tendons warm up.
- A 'bump' on your tendon.
- A crackling or creaking sound when you touch or move your Achilles tendon.

HOW TO REHABILITATE IT

Apply the principles of RICE and take a break from sport for at least two weeks. Then do these strengthening moves once a day.

  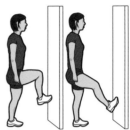

STRAIGHT-LEG CALF LOWERING

- Stand with the balls of your feet on the edge of a step. Hold on to a support if necessary.
- Rise up onto your toes, then remove the unaffected leg from the step so you're holding the tiptoe position.
- Take five seconds to lower your affected heel as far down as is comfortable. Do three sets of 15 twice a day.

WHY?
A study at the University Hospital of Northern Sweden found that 12 weeks of this and the following exercise combined could help eradicate Achilles pain.

BENT-LEG CALF LOWERING

- Sit on a chair, place a weight on top of your thighs and rest the balls of your feet on a ledge or step.
- Rise up onto your toes then remove the unaffected leg from the step so you're on tiptoes on the sore leg.
- Lower your affected heel as far downwards as is comfortable. Do three sets of 15 twice a day.

WHY?
Doing this exercise with a bent leg forces your deep calf muscle to work, which strengthens the major calf muscles needed to help heal Achilles tendonitis.

STANDING WALL STRETCH

- Stand with both feet parallel to each other roughly hip-width apart, facing a wall at about arm's-length away.
- Put the affected foot on the wall at knee height and try to press its heel against the wall as flat as you can.
- Lift your chest until you are standing straight. Hold this position for three minutes on each leg.

WHY?
A study in the journal *Foot & Ankle International* found that holding an Achilles tendon stretch for this exact period of time helped to reduce pain.

HOW LONG UNTIL YOU'RE RECOVERED?

According to Jenkins, these are the recovery rates of Achilles tendonitis, depending on the severity of your injury.

MILD INJURY	100% AFTER 2-10 DAYS
AVERAGE INJURY	100% AFTER 7-8 WEEKS
SEVERE INJURY	100% AFTER 3-6 MONTHS

PLANTAR FASCIITIS

PAIN, EXPLAINED
Dr Ross Sherman reveals why the underside of your foot hurts.

1 FEELING PAIN?
This is an overuse injury so you won't remember any particular incident where you've damaged your heel. Pointers could include increased training frequency/intensity or adding hill sprints.

2 PLANTAR FASCIA
It's a thick, broad band of tissue that runs along the bottom of your foot. It supports your foot's arch and acts like a shock-absorbing bow-string. When a high load is forced on it you can get a small split in it.

3 WAKE UP!
At the time, this rip will only create mild discomfort, which you probably won't even notice. But when you sleep, your body starts the repair process – making the plantar fascia stiff. Upon waking, it will be inflexible. When you take your first strides you'll stretch too far and tear it slightly.

4 HEEL
The tear can lead to additional micro-tearing, which results in the stinging pain at the base of your heel pad, which can last all day if you're on your feet.

CAUSE & **EFFECT**
Why it happens and how you are able to spot it

WHAT CAUSES IT?
The American Academy of Orthopaedic Surgeons cites these as the root:

- Standing for long periods
- Poor foot mechanics,
- Being overweight places additional pressure on your plantar fascia
- Tight calves that limit the amount you can flex your ankles
- A big increase in training load
- Arthritis causes inflammation in the tendons at the bottom of your foot
- Diabetes – less blood gets to your feet
- Poor or worn-out running shoes

SPOT IT!
Research at the Mayo Clinic, US, found it's likely you have plantar fasciitis if you experience one or more of the following symptoms:

- A sharp pain occurring in the inside of the bottom of your heel, which may spread under your whole foot.
- Heel pain when you get up and walk after waking, stand or climb stairs.
- Intense heel pain after long periods of being on your feet or after getting up out of a chair.
- Mild swelling in your heel.

HOW TO REHABILITATE IT

Rest from all weight-bearing sporting activities for two to three weeks. Then do these moves from Sherman two to three times a week.

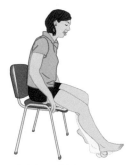

FOOT ROLL

- Sit on a chair and place either a tin of food (on its side) or a tennis ball on the floor in front of you.
- Rest the arch of your injured foot on the tin or tennis ball and press down while rolling the tin/ball up and down from your heel to your mid-arch.
- Perform this for one minute, rest for 30 seconds then repeat twice more. Increase gradually as your injury heals.

WHY?

'This lengthens and softens the plantar fascia in order to release the pressure that's magnifying the heel pain,' says Sherman.

TOE FLEXES

- Sit with your injured leg straight out in front of you. Loop a towel around your foot, holding the ends with both hands.
- Ensuring the towel goes around the arch of your foot, pull it tightly towards you.
- Keeping your injured knee straight, push your foot away from your body and apply resistance with the towel. Do three sets of 10 repetitions.

WHY?

'The force from the towel against your plantar fascia stretches it out, to provide a two-pronged approach to fast recovery,' says Sherman.

PLANTAR STRETCH

- Cross your legs and put your affected ankle above your opposite knee, with the underside of your foot is facing you.
- Grab hold of your toes on the raised foot closest to you and pull them back with both hands.
- Hold this position for 10 seconds then release. Repeat 10 times. Do three to six times a day, starting when you get up.

WHY?

'After subjects did this for eight weeks there was a dramatic improvement,' says orthopaedic surgeon Dr Ben DiGiovanni.

HOW LONG UNTIL YOU'RE RECOVERED?

According to studies in the *American Family Physician Journal*, the following are the expected recovery rates.

MILD INJURY	100% AFTER 2-6 MONTHS
AVERAGE INJURY	100% AFTER 9-12 MONTHS
SEVERE INJURY	100% AFTER 18 MONTHS

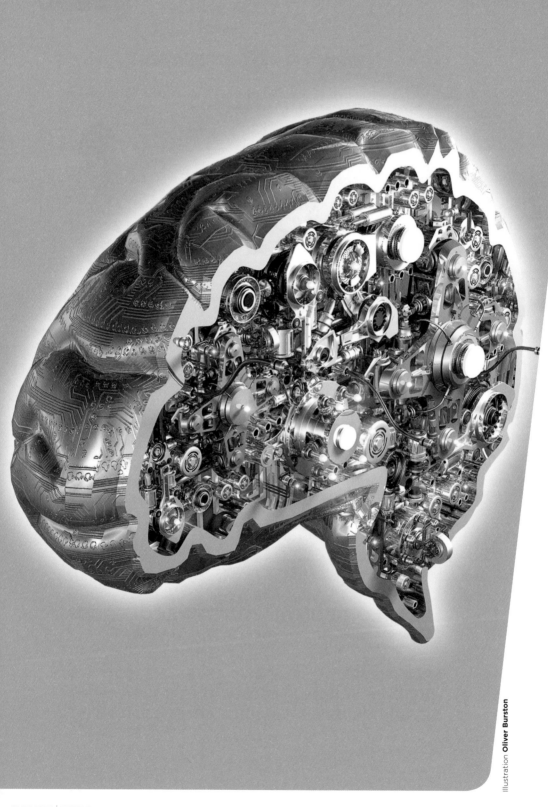

Illustration **Oliver Burston**

MOTIVATION

Your brain is one of your most powerful running allies. Here's how to get it working for you

ICE RUNNER
Turn a cold run
into a hot date

48 WAYS TO KEEP *GOING*

There are many reasons for loss of motivation, but no excuses. Be inspired with these tips, stories and more

1 START A BLOG
Post your daily mileage online, then pass the link on to your friends and family. Do you really want Auntie Susan or Uncle Bob asking why you skipped your four-miler on Wednesday?

2 FORGET TIME
Running coach Shane Bogan advises leaving your watch at home once in a while. 'It's liberating not to be worried about pace,' he says. Just enjoy a run for its own sake.

3 TREAT YOURSELF
That new running watch you're hankering after? Go ahead and buy it – after timing 10 more speed sessions with your old one.

4 LOOK TO THE PAST
Emil Zatopek, who won four Olympic gold medals in his career, was a tough-as-nails athlete known for his intense training methods, such as running in work boots. Competing with a gland infection and against his doctor's orders, the Czech won three distance events, including the marathon, at the 1952 Helsinki Olympics in Finland.

5 THINK FAST
The runners coach Christy Coughlin works with always get a boost from this simple negative-split workout: run for 20 minutes as slowly as you want, then turn around and run home faster. 'The long warm-up helps you feel great and run faster on the way back,' says Coughlin.

6 BLAZE A NEW PATH
'If you do the same runs all the time, it can beat you down,' says Alan Culpepper, an Olympic marathon runner. Try a GPS system, or check out mapmyrun.com to find new routes.

7 GET YOUR KIT ON
The simple act of throwing on the appropriate clothes will get you out the door. You can take them off again, after you've run around and sweated in them a bit.

8 ENTER A RELAY RACE
Either as part of a large running team, or do the run leg of a triathlon with a cycling and a swimming friend. You'll be less likely to skimp on your training as you won't want to let your teammates down.

9 SIGN UP FOR A WINTER RACE...
...or a running holiday in a warm country. Every training mile you log takes you closer to an active break away from the cold. Great choices include Bangkok (bkmarathon.com) or Las Vegas (runrocknroll.com).

10 DEVISE YOUR OWN LOYALTY SCHEME
Try one mile equals one point. Start collecting today and soon you could have saved up enough points for a new pair of running shoes, an afternoon at a health spa, a ticket to the big game or a guilt-free blow out from your favourite eatery. ❯

11 FEEL INSPIRED

In 1949, nine-year-old Wilma Rudolph learned to walk without leg braces after suffering from polio and spending most of her first years in bed. Rudolph went on to win three gold medals for the USA in the 1960 Olympics.

12 SET SOME DAILY GOALS

Scott Jurek, seven-time winner of the Western States 100-Mile Endurance Run in the US, sets himself a variety of goals for big races and for training sessions. 'Maybe it is a technique goal, maybe a pace goal, maybe a goal of running faster at the end,' he says.

13 SPOIL YOURSELF

Book a massage for the day after your long run. It's very good for your muscles and can be considered as an appropriate treat after all that hard running.

14 RUN WHEN IT'S TIPPING DOWN

Trust us – with rain lashing down on you and the wind whipping you across your face, you will feel wonderfully alive. Just make sure that you have a spare kit and a dry pair of shoes for tomorrow's wet-weather run.

15 FOR EMERGENCY USE ONLY

Consider taking a short break from running if you think you've got the beginning of an injury or you're truly fatigued. A couple of day's rest may reinvigorate you. Call this one instant running motivation for three days from now.

16 YOU WANT TO LOOK GOOD ON THE BEACH

It may not be at the top of your list but it's certainly a good motivator – especially if you've a holiday coming up.

17 IT'S SUMMER!

Well, it may not be when you read this, but when it is, go outside and run. Read the rest of this later.

18 IT'S NEVER TOO LATE

Mary Peters was 33 and near the end of her career when she defeated local favourite Heide Rosendahl to take gold in the pentathlon at the 1972 Olympics in Munich. Her victory brought temporary calmness to Northern Ireland, with rival factions celebrating together the country's greatest ever sporting success.

19 GET PAID

Set a price for attaining a certain mileage. When you hit it, pay up. Keep the money in a jar, and once it accumulates, buy that new running jacket.

20 IF YOU'RE REALLY IN THE MOOD...

...for a change, check out the list of clothing-optional races and other running events at bn.org.uk.

21 WATCH THIS:

Endurance – a 1999 docudrama that shows how Ethiopian Haile Gebrselassie became one of the best distance runners of all time.

22 EXERCISE MAKES SEX BETTER

According to thorough research. Enough said.

23 GET WET

If it gets too hot outside, coach Bruce Gross suggests logging your miles by running in the deep end of a pool while wearing a flotation vest. Gross tells his runners to break it up by going hard for five minutes, then resting for one minute. Start slowly and build up to an hour.

24 REMEMBER, RACE RESULTS STAY ON GOOGLE FOREVER

Well, until the end of either the internet or the world, anyway. Need any more motivation to clock the best time you can? ▧

RICH RUNNING
Turn your hobby
into a money-
making machine

25 TURN THINGS AROUND

'A poor performance is a strong motivator for me,' says elite marathon runner Clint Verran. 'I can't wait to prove to myself that I'm a better runner than my last showing.' Verran also says negative comments from his coaches fire him up. 'For me, proving somebody else to be wrong is key.'

26 RUN LOADS OF MARATHONS?

Maybe try an ultra. Or a mile.

27 BECOME A RUNNING MENTOR

Once you get a friend hooked on your sport they'll be counting on your continued support and guidance. And you someone to run with.

28 IF YOU ARE STAYING IN

The Four-Minute Mile is a 1988 UK film that tells the story of how Roger Bannister became the first man to run the mile in under four minutes, despite conventional wisdom of the time insisting that such an achievement was physiologically impossible.

29 DUST OFF YOUR TRACK SPIKES

Some athletics clubs organise Olympic-style summer games where you can compete in events like the mile or even the 400-metre hurdles.

30 REMEMBER THE SIMPLE TRUTH

That you almost always feel better after a run than you do before it.

31 MAKE A CONNECTION

Try logging on to dateactive. co.uk, a website that connects active people looking for love. Get in your run and go on a date at the same time.

32 DON'T EXPECT TO IMPROVE AFTER EVERY RUN

Some days will be slower than others, and some days might hurt a bit more than others.

But as long as you're out there running, it's a good day.

33 RUN A BATH...

...on a freezing morning then head out for a three-miler. The sooner you get back, the hotter the bath.

34 JUST... START!

If the thought of running your full session is too much to bear, just go out to run around the block. Chances are, once you're outside, you'll start to feel better and put in at least a few miles.

35 FORGET ABOUT THE BIG PICTURE

Every now and then put away the training manual and set aside your race calendar. Stop overthinking it all, and just run for today.

36 FOCUS ON THE COMPETITION

Shawn Crawford, the 2004 Olympic 200m gold medallist, says his two chief competitors are himself and his stopwatch, and they keep him heading out every day. 'I want to break records, and you can't break records sitting on the sofa at home.'

37 IT AIN'T OVER 'TIL IT'S OVER

Roger Bannister and John Landy raced at 1954's British Empire and Commonwealth Games in Vancouver. For most of The Miracle Mile, as it was called, Landy was in the lead, but Bannister took him on the final turn. And the moral of this story? Never give up.

38 BECOME A RACE DIRECTOR

If you live in a small town with no road races, start your own. Tie it into a local annual celebration in the summer, and work with local track and cross-country teams to help promote it.

39 STOP RUNNING IN CIRCLES

Andy Steinfeld, who coaches marathon runners, says group point-to-point runs are a fun way to add a new twist to training. His runners head out for 12-20 miles, then refuel together at a local restaurant before hopping on the bus to travel back to the starting point.

40 LIVE IN THE NOW

Ultrarunner Scott Jurek focuses on the moment to get him through difficult patches on his long runs and races. 'I tune in to my breath, my technique and my current pace, and I stay away from what lies ahead,' he says. This is an especially helpful technique when what lies ahead is another 99 miles.

41 GET SOME PERSPECTIVE

LEAP OF FAITH
Leave the training plan behind and just go for a run

Meb Keflezighi, the Eritrean-born US runner and 2014 Boston Marathon winner, listens to songs about his former country's struggle for independence from Ethiopia when he needs a boost. 'The true heroes are the soldiers,' he says. 'Those are the real tough guys.'

42 BRING HOME SOME HARDWARE

OK, so you're not going to win the London Marathon, but that doesn't mean you can't score a medal. Find a few small races where you might be able to compete for the top spots in your age group.

43 BUY A FULL-LENGTH MIRROR

Make sure you look in it every day. If you're running regularly (and eating well) you will soon see changes to your body composition that make you want to carry on.

44 TRY A TRI

By doing a portion of your weekly miles as triathlon training – swimming and cycling – you'll reinvigorate your mind, body and spirit. As well as improve your running.

45 INVEST IN SOME GOOD GEAR

For beginners, this may mean a good pair of running shoes to avoid injuries and technical clothes made of fabric that wicks away moisture and prevents chafing. For others, experimenting with the latest GPS unit or foot pod can be a fun way to stay motivated.

46 BE CREATIVE

If the idea of going on your regular four-miler just sinks you further into the sofa, remember that there are plenty of other ways to get the miles in. Such as playing football: a midfielder can run up to six miles in a 90-minute game.

47 IGNORE THE DIRTY DISHES

They can wait until the sun goes down, your run can't. This goes for laundry too.

48 LET US HELP

Visit runnersworld.co.uk for pages of ideas and inspiration from the experts. ◼

BEAT THE
CLOCKS

As a nation, we're time poor – these tips will help you squeeze running into the busiest of schedules

Photography **Chris Korbey** Illustration **Fredrik Broden**

With so much to do in everyday life, running can sometimes get pushed out. Lack of time – whether actual or perceived – is the biggest barrier to keeping on top of your training. We're here to help.

Time problems will fall into the three categories below: Making Time (questions of when, where and how); Saving Time (little dos and don'ts that add up to serious savings); and Rethinking Time (adjusting the relationship between the amount of running you do and the time you need to do it).

Here's the plan: there are 25 time-management tips in these three categories. Pick any three of the strategies – one from each section – and try them for a month. If any work, great; if not, pick three more. If you try them all and still can't find time to run, you probably don't really want to. Which is a shame. Chances are, however, you'll find some that work every time. So stop clock watching and get your kit on!

MAKING TIME

Here are some tips to help you claw back some time along with ways to get those around you assisting too.

1 PLAN YOUR WEEK
Sit down with your diary on a Sunday and draw up a training schedule, before the blank spaces start filling up with other priorities.

2 THINK QUALITY, NOT QUANTITY
Make the most out of what you have. Finding time for a 20-minute run is easy. Just make every minute count. Alternate one minute a little faster than your normal pace with one-minute recoveries. Do a two- to four-minute warm-up first and a similar cool-down afterwards.

3 GET UP 30 MINUTES EARLIER
Run before anyone else is even out of bed. An early morning run will invigorate you for the day ahead.

4 IF YOU POSSIBLY CAN, GET A DOG
Not everyone has the space or the hours at home to make one practical, but if your circumstances allow, canines make great training partners. Trust us, you'll be literally dragged out the door.

5 SWAP YOUR DUTIES
One morning, afternoon or evening, let your other half look after the children while you run. If your other half runs or has their own hobbies, you can reverse roles the day after. Or...

6 ...TAKE THE KIDS WITH YOU
Many gyms now offer in-house nurseries. In 90 minutes, you can squeeze in an hour on the treadmill and a 20-minute circuit-training session on the weight machines — an excellent all-round workout that will improve strength, conditioning and endurance. And your children should get a bit of exercise into the bargain as well.

7 GIVE 'EM THE RUNAROUND
While the children are playing football (or whatever), run loops around the field. 'I do this twice a week,' says mother-of-two Judie Simpson. 'Once as a steady one-hour run. The second time I'll pick it up on the long side of the field and jog the short side for 45 minutes.' Don't forget to cheer if your offspring scores, though.

8 BEAT THE RUSH HOUR
If your commute is of a doable running distance take your kit into work and run home. While everyone else is ▶

stuck in gridlock you'll be speeding past traffic and ticking off a training session in the process. By the time you're home you'll be de-stressed from the rigours of the day and can allow yourself to feel slightly smug.

9 SET SHORT-TERM GOALS

Too many runners think too far ahead when laying out their training. 'Instead, set a fortnightly goal, and make it specific: run three times a week for the next two weeks.' says Dave Scott, six-time Ironman Hawaii winner.

10 PLACE YOUR BETS

People who bet £25 that they could stick with their training programme for six months had a 97 per cent success rate in a study at Michigan State University in the US. Bet against a friend, and the first to give up pays up.

11 THINK LITTLE AND OFTEN

If you're new to it, aim for frequency, not duration. Instead of trying to find time for a 45-minute run two or three times a week, do shorter sessions of 15-20 minutes.

12 GO LONGER TO GET STRONGER

Veteran runners should focus on two key runs a week, sessions where they really push. Try a one-hour interval session (or hills or fartlek) in the week and then long a run at the weekend. Fill in around them with short, easy runs, cross-training and rest days.

13 FIND A FRIEND

If someone is expecting you to show up, you're less likely to make excuses.

SAVING TIME

Fifteen seconds here, a minute there; it may not seem like much, but you'll be surprised how quickly it all adds up.

14 THINK AHEAD

Get your kit ready the night before. Even loosen your laces so your feet slide straight into your shoes. That way, you sit down and dress for battle quickly. No back-and-forth from bedroom to laundry and back to bedroom, tracking down something clean to wear before you go.

15 GET READY FOR BREKKIE

Plop your smoothie ingredients in a blender the night before an early morning run and put it in the fridge. After your run, hit the switch and eight seconds later... breakfast is served. We tried this ourselves: assembling from scratch in the morning took 1:53, meaning we saved a total of 1:45.

16 HOLD OFF ON THE STRETCHES

Don't spend valuable time stretching cold muscles before you train. Instead, walk briskly for a few minutes, then jog slowly to start your run.

17 RUN BEFORE YOU TALK

You meet your running partners and start talking while doing some ineffectual trunk twists as a warm-up. Don't do it. Say hello (it's only polite), and start jogging slowly. Talk then, before the pace picks up. Do all four of these tips from 14 to 17 and you save up to 10 minutes – enough time to turn a five-

mile run into a six-miler. Over the course of a week, you net at least 35 minutes of extra running time.

18 KEEP YOUR SHORTS ON

'Wear shorts as underwear, says US running guru Jeff Galloway, so you're run-ready the instant your antennae pick up a 10-minute block of free time. 'Accumulate enough short runs and they add up,' he says. A study at Stanford University, US, found multiple bouts of moderate exercise produce significant effects. Leading us nicely on to...

DON'T THROW IN THE TOWEL IF LIFE GETS BUSY – YOU CAN FIT IN A RUN SOMEWHERE

6　　　7　　　8　9

13　　14

20

27

RUNNING TO PLAN
Shift your week
around to make
room for training

RETHINKING TIME

Some attitudes towards running and/or ourselves stop us working out. Think differently to get ahead.

22 BE REALISTIC
Cut back on your running if you need to. But don't throw in the towel because life gets busy. Ride these periods out, and fit in a run of some kind — 15 minutes, 10 minutes — every second or third day. Resume a more intense routine when you can. When your schedule implodes, short-term changes can stop you fretting your way into being a sofa sloth.

23 BE A BIT SELFISH
By giving your run a high priority — not just in your day but in your life also — you boost your physical and emotional health, and live up to your obligation to your family to be healthy and happy. Let them know what's good for you can be of benefit to them as well.

24 BE FLEXIBLE
If circumstances change, don't make excuses to ditch your planned run. If a surprise meeting cancels the lunch time jog, do it after work. If you miss the alarm, take your kit to work and run at lunch time. And 'I don't feel like it' doesn't wash. 'If you really want to run, you'll find the time,' says former 2:09 marathoner Ron Hill. 'It's really no different than finding time to shave, eat or read the morning paper.'

25 HAVE FUN!
Enjoying a run greatly increases the likelihood that you'll want to — and will — find time for the next one. Run a new route; reverse an old one. If you usually run on roads, head for the park and run through the trees. Variety really is the spice of life, so mix it up when you are pounding out the miles. ■

19 DIVIDE AND CONQUER
On busy days, beat the clock by breaking up your run into two shorter sessions. Instead of a single 40-minute run, maybe do 20 in the morning and again at lunchtime, or whatever fits your schedule.

20 TURN DOWN THE VOLUME
Runners clocking up 50 miles a week had marathon times no faster than those who logged 10 miles less, found a study at the University of Northern Iowa in the US. Surprisingly, more isn't always better, so

don't scramble to find time for miles simply to pad out your weekly total.

21 THE 10-MINUTE MIRACLE
'Run at a faster than normal training pace (but don't sprint) for 10 footfalls of your right foot. When you reach 10, do 10 more steps of easy jogging,' says exercise physiologist Jack Daniels. Then do 20-20 and so on up to 60-60. Then work back to 10-10. This is a good way to warm up, cool down and throw in some intensity in a short space of time.

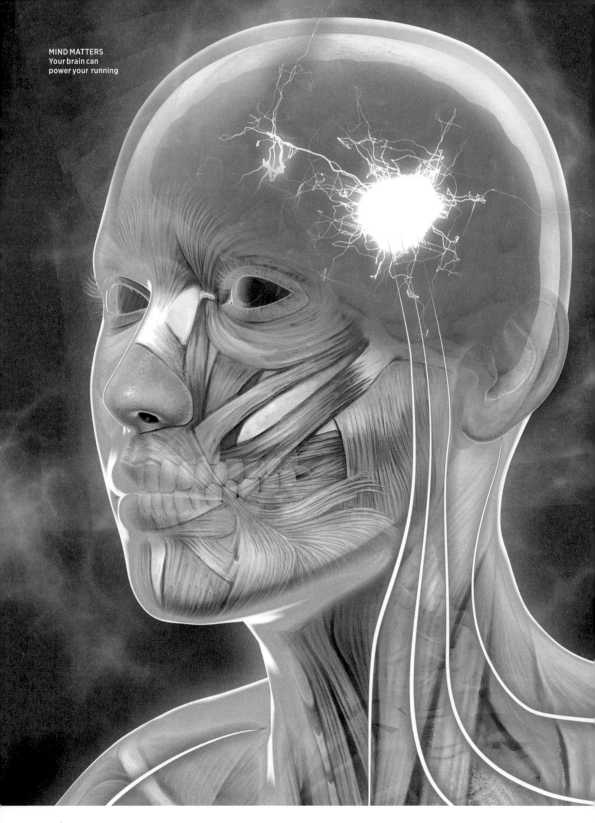

MIND MATTERS
Your brain can
power your running

QUICK
THINKING

Training your mind is as important as improving your body. Here's how it can help you go faster

You know it all too well: that awful moment when your overworked lungs and leaden lower limbs combine to create an overbearing desire to S-L-O-W D-O-W-N. When the burden of placing one foot in front of the other grows intensely with every limping stride and you reach the end of your run – far earlier than intended – convinced that you just don't have another step in you. You are, to use the scientific parlance, absolutely knackered.

Given where these go-slow sensations manifest, it's unsurprising that most research into improving endurance has been based primarily around the theory that fatigue occurs as a result of the body – the muscles, lungs and heart – letting your brain know that it has reached its limit. But what if that turns out to be a false assumption? What if it's the other way around?

Acknowledging the role your mind plays in reaching peak athletic performance is nothing new. Though it's somewhat intangible, elite athletes have long exalted the merits of mental power in eking out a physical edge that can mean the difference between a podium finish and also-ran. Sir Roger Bannister, a man who knows a thing or two about pushing the performance envelope, even hinted beyond the notion of willpower: 'It is the brain, and not the heart or lungs, that is the critical organ.'

GREY MATTERS

A growing number of scientists are now in agreement, and many have centered studies on the precise role of the brain when it comes to endurance performance and fatigue. Among the first was Tim Noakes, professor of exercise and sports at the University of Cape Town and author of *Lore of Running* (£20, Human Kinetics Europe). Based on his findings, he argues that it is the brain that limits our endurance efforts long before the body gives out.

'But what about VO_2 max?' you may ask, quite possibly in snatched breaths, bent double by the side of a track. After all, scientists and coaches have been pushing us to our lung-bursting limits based on the theory that a lack of oxygen to the working muscles is what limits performance since Nobel Prize-winning British physiologist AV Hill presented the basis for that theory almost 100 years ago. The idea that oxygen delivery is the whole story seems neat and logical. But it's wrong, contends Noakes, who first challenged Hill's model as far back as ▶

1987. In research published in the journal *Medicine & Science in Sports & Exercise*, Noakes reanalysed Hill's data and discovered that Hill's studies hadn't actually proven that runners had run out of oxygen.

So what is happening? Noakes's own research-based theory on endurance performance is known as the 'central governor' model. When it comes to fatigue's red stop light, he says, your brain isn't merely receiving the information, it's in control. 'Fatigue is just a sensation – it's your brain telling your body it's tired, not the other way round,' says Noakes. And how does the brain pull rank on your brawn? 'It inhibits force output by reducing drive to the muscles,' says Noakes, which cuts the number of motor units that are activated during exercise. In other words, your brain tells your muscles to slow down, rather than your muscles telling your brain that it's time to rest.

If this alternative theory of muscle fatigue is correct, the significance is huge. But first things first – is the research there to back it up? Studying the levels of electrical activity in working muscles does provide compelling evidence: theoretically, as muscle fibres tire, more should be recruited to pick up the slack. However, in a study that required experienced cyclists to perform 1,000m and 4,000m sprints over the course of a 100K time trial, Noakes noted that electrical activity in the muscles actually dropped as fatigue set in – even when the cyclists were pedalling as fast as they could. 'They felt as though they'd reached their physical limits, but they were actually only using 30 per cent of their muscle fibres,' says Noakes.

Noakes isn't on his own here. A University of Birmingham study revealed even more about the brain's tendency to ring-fence our energy supplies. Athletes were asked to rinse their mouths with (but not swallow) either a solution of water and a flavourless carbohydrate called maltodextrin, or a placebo. Those who had swished the carb-based solution improved their performance in intense bouts of exercise lasting an hour or so. It appears that the brain can sense carbohydrates in the mouth, even tasteless ones, says Matt Bridge, a senior sports science lecturer at the university. 'Your brain tells your body that carbohydrates are on the way. And with that message, muscles and nerves are prompted to work harder and longer.' Remember, the carbs were not consumed, so there was no actual fuel boost. It was, as they say, all in the mind.

So why, exactly, is our grey matter so keen to slow us down that it pulls one over on us? According to Noakes's central governor model, our brains are constantly keeping an eye on the bigger picture – stopping us pushing past the point where we have the potential to do harm to muscles or other organs. To guard against an internal catastrophe, 'a control system in a small area of the brain constantly monitors the signals sent from all over your body,' says Noakes. If it interprets the information as a threat, your brain produces feelings of discomfort and reduces electrical output to the muscles to keep you safe.'

That's when those fairly convincing 'I must stop right now' messages start bouncing around inside your head. You may feel them as coming express mail from your searing quads and stabbing calves, but they've actually never ventured to the business end of your running machinery. In fact, 'those messages are sent from the sub-conscious brain to the conscious brain,' says Noakes.

THE EXTRA YARDS IN YOUR HEAD

The central governor theory may explain the phenomenon of seemingly utterly exhausted marathoners somehow finding enough gas in their tanks to rally for the final mile. Noakes suggests that the subconscious brain

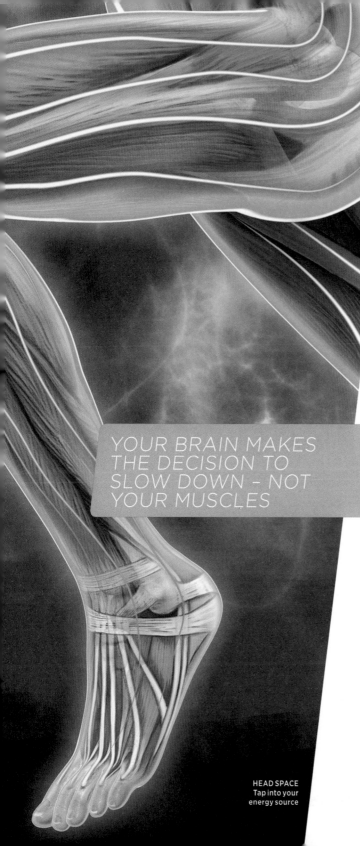

YOUR BRAIN MAKES
THE DECISION TO
SLOW DOWN – NOT
YOUR MUSCLES

HEAD SPACE
Tap into your
energy source

senses the end of exercise is near, so it allows any extra energy to be released for use by your muscles. This regulation mechanism is there to ensure you always reach the finish line safely, says Noakes. 'You always have a little reserve.'

So far, so geeky. But there's an obvious practical question popping up here: if we know that there's rest and refuelling on the way, and we know that there's more in reserve than our subconscious brain wants us to get access to, can we short-circuit the subconscious safety catch and tap into that extra potential? The knowledge that there's more in the tank than our brains want to let on is pretty empowering in itself, but is there something we can do to trick our subconscious into halting the feelings of fatigue and removing the physiological shackles to let more muscle fibres get involved in moving us from A to B, ASAP?

The tantalising promise is that we can con our grey matter into giving us more oomph when we need it. But how do you get one over on your (central) guv'nor? A little trickery goes a long way, according to a Northumbria University study. Researchers put cyclists through a 4,000m time challenge; after several repeats, participants felt they understood their limits over the distance. Next, each of the cyclists was presented with two avatars on a screen in front of them. One moved at the rate of their own pedalling, while their virtual competitor, they were told, was programmed to move at the pace of their own best effort – but it was actually travelling one per cent faster. The cyclists ended up matching their speedier avatars on their virtual rides, achieving faster times than they had previously been able to.

'A small deception of the brain can enhance your performance,' says Professor Kevin Thompson, head of sport and exercise sciences at Northumbria University. 'Despite the internal feedback ▷

to the brain being heightened by the extra power output being produced, the study subjects still believed that it was possible to beat their virtual opponent.'

But it obviously only goes so far. No matter how cunning you become at outmanoeuvring your brain, the energy reserves it can dip into are still limited, says Noakes. 'Ultimately, physiological forces will always have the final say over the brain.'

Using the same approach as before, Dr Thompson attempted to find out where that physiological line is drawn. Again, two groups of cyclists competed against an avatar, but while the first group were told the second avatar would be racing either two or five per cent harder than their best efforts, the second group were kept in the dark about the increase in speed. The first group gave up the chase almost from the off, only matching their own best efforts. The second group, however, kept up with the avatars that were programmed to perform two per cent harder, but five per cent proved too much, with the cyclists giving up halfway through.

ACCESS YOUR EMERGENCY POWER

So, what does this mean for you? 'Our findings demonstrate that a metabolic reserve exists which, if it can be accessed, can release a performance improvement of between two and five per cent,' says Thompson. 'At a competitive level, an average speed increase of just one per cent can make a massive difference.'

The lesson is that if muscle fatigue does originate in the brain, then your efforts to prevent fatigue should target your mind as well as your muscles. And central to this, says Noakes, is convincing your brain of your actual ability. 'Coaches have known this for a long time,' he says. 'They teach people to train harder so their brains learn what they're capable of.'

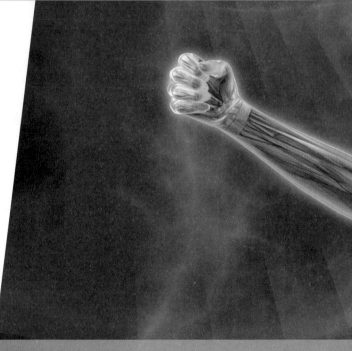

A SMALL DECEPTION OF THE BRAIN CAN ENHANCE YOUR PERFORMANCE

MIND *GAINS*

Use these psychological tricks to fool your brain into releasing

REDEFINE YOUR LIMITS
Show your brain what your body can really do

You may think you consciously decided how fast you ran today but you didn't. At the University of Cape Town, two groups of cyclists completed time trials in the hot and the cold. Those exercising in the heat clocked slower times – but they dropped pace well before their core temperatures rose significantly. This suggests pace is preemptively set by the brain. How can you counter this? There's no way to sugarcoat it: learn to deal with discomfort the hard way, says Noakes. Running at race pace and faster in 1,000m intervals is the best way to show your brain what your body can do.

FREE SOME HEADSPACE
Tough day? Time to reach for the remote...

Give yourself a performance boost with *The Great British Bake Off*. Yes, you heard that right. Disengaging your brain for a little while could give you an edge in the track or field. In a Bangor University study, athletes were asked to perform high-intensity sessions after spending 90 minutes watching a documentary or completing a hard problem-solving task. While physiological responses barely differed between the groups, the more mentally fatigued athletes had higher levels of perceived exertion and gave up 15 per cent earlier than the TV watchers.

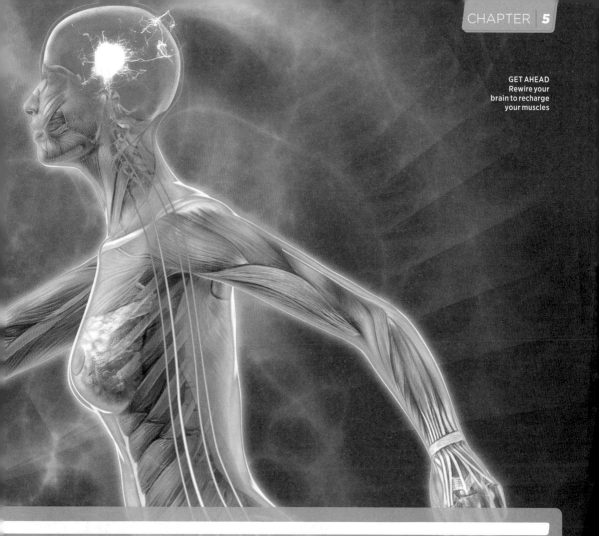

GET AHEAD
Rewire your
brain to recharge
your muscles

your performance reserve

STRENGTH IN NUMBERS
Take on a friend to tap into your fuel reserves

Portsmouth University researchers asked cyclists to race as fast as they could for 2,000m, as a figure representing them moved along a virtual course on a screen. Next, they were told a second figure would represent the efforts of a competitor. The cyclists stormed to victory over their 'rivals' with an average speed increase of one and a half per cent over the final stages. 'Our results show that competition provides the motivation to tell the brain to eat into a greater part of the fuel reserve that athletes have left at the end of a race,' says study author Dr Jo Corbett, a physiologist.

REST, ASSURED
Banish mental fatigue with proper recovery

Hard training sessions release cytokines – immune-system cells that aid the repair of exercise-related muscle damage. One of these (IL-6) enters the brain and alters our neurochemistry, causing exhaustion. Researchers at Appalachian State University in the US discovered that high-intensity training, with insufficient rest afterwards, causes levels of IL-6 to stay elevated, which can leave you extremely fatigued. Always get your full quota of shut-eye (eight hours during heavy training periods) and find time for a healthy post-run meal – see *Head Candy*, on page 172.

MIND OVER MATTER
Meditate away your aches and pains

Taking time out to say 'ommm' can relieve the ouch, according to US studies at Wake Forest Baptist Medical Centre. Regular meditation was found to reduce 'pain intensity' by 40 per cent and 'pain unpleasantness' by 57 per cent. And brain scans demonstrated reduced pain-related activation. The trick is to let your mind run wild and acknowledge all your thoughts, says study author Fadel Zeidan, but without dwelling on them. Pay close attention to your breathing, says Zeidan. 'Follow [the air] as it enters at your nose; notice any tingling – scan your body for sensations.' ■

BRAIN TRAIN
Let your body
boost your mind
through running

ONE TRACK
MIND

A complete rundown of the wonders worked on our
brains by the simple act of propelling ourselves forward

Illustrations **Oliver Burston**

From the initial hit of the endorphin high to stimulating your creativity and concentration, all the way to warding off dementia, running matters to your grey matter. So if your body is rebelling, here are 10 reasons why your mind will thank you for pushing past those aches and pains and making the effort.

SMARTEN UP
Big meeting in the diary? Get your running shoes on. US researchers from the University of Illinois found going for a run improved reasoning ability, while a study at National Taiwan Sport University has pinpointed 30 minutes of moderate exercise as the ideal duration and intensity to optimise cognitive performance immediately afterwards.

But you may not have to wait until you're done to reap the rewards, as recent University of Aberdeen research found that the act of running triggers creative thinking. According to the researchers, the mechanism at work here is that your brain associates forward motion with the future. The study also found that to maximise the effect you should stick to a route you know well, so worrying about directions doesn't limit your mind's capacity to wander. Also, keep the effort easy, as maintaining speed and tracking splits will divert much-needed brain power away from creativity.

GET HIGH
If your sweat-elevated smarts aren't enough to put a smile on your face, then perhaps the fabled runner's high will do the trick. German research has traced the effect to regions of the brain releasing natural opiates as we run. (These regions also become active in response to emotions such as love.) Other studies have shown the sweet spot for endorphin production is a comfortably hard effort (think tempo run), while research at Oxford University found exercising in groups could increase endorphin release.

And there's more bliss-inducing chemistry bubbling away; running also triggers your brain to release substances called endocannabinoids, which promote feelings of calm. Challenging but not all-out efforts (70-85 per cent of maximum heart rate) are the key to this drawer in your brain's natural pharmacy.

STAY HAPPY
Unlike other chemical shortcuts to happiness, pounding the pavement doesn't come with a comedown. In fact, research shows that regular running reduces stress and elevates mood over the long term. A study published in *Medicine & Science in Sports & Exercise* identified increased levels of tryptophan in runners – elevated tryptophan is typically paralleled by increased levels of the mood-elevating neurotransmitter serotonin. Another study, published in the *Journal of Sports Medicine and Physical* ◢

Fitness, found physical activity helped to lower patients' score on the Depression, Anxiety and Stress Scale (DASS).

Other research has found that regular running can be as effective as prescription antidepressants (or in some cases even more so), acting in the same way as the medication by causing mood-improving neurotransmitters such as serotonin and norepinephrine to stay in the system for longer.

BEAT CRAVINGS

Mental visions of post-run pasta may power you through your miles, but on a brain-chemistry level running can actually aid the systems that prevent you from overindulging. A study at the University of Western Australia found intense interval training was most effective in regulating appetite. The researchers think this could be down to exercise curtailing production of 'the hunger hormone', ghrelin. Other studies have shown working out in the heat is more effective in reducing appetite, so if curbing calorie intake is high on your priority list, consider the treadmill on winter days.

If your vices go beyond the biscuit tin, then there's more good news: when scanning the brains of smokers, University of Plymouth researchers found that the areas associated with addiction showed less activity post-exercise.

MEMORY JOG

One particular area of the brain where a wealth of research has established the potential benefits of running is the hippocampus, which is associated with learning and memory. One such study, conducted by Japanese researchers and published in the *International Journal of Sports Medicine*, showed regular moderate exercise improved hippocampus-related memory in rats but, interestingly, rodents who picked up the intensity and did all their running faster

than lactate threshold pace didn't do any better in memory tests than a sedentary control group. The scientists put this down to the stress of consistent hard training diverting the rats' physiological resources to recovery rather than buffing up brain systems, and they believe the same would hold true in humans.

BUILD BRAIN POWER...

Running does more than keep your existing grey matter well oiled; it could also trigger the growth of new brain tissue. Exercise drives the growth of brand new nerve cells (neurogenesis) and blood vessels (angiogenesis), which combine to increase brain tissue volume, according to researchers at the University of Maryland, US. This is crucial, as research has shown that we begin to lose brain tissue after our late 20s. More specifically, a study published in the *Proceedings of the National Academy of Sciences* found regular exercisers increased the volume of their hippocampus – that part of the brain linked to learning and memory – by two per cent, compared with their inactive peers. That's big news, as it was previously thought that this region of your grey matter couldn't grow at all after childhood.

...AND HOLD ON TO IT

Staying fit as you age is vital in keeping your brain in good shape. A study published in *Frontiers in Aging Neuroscience* found higher cardio-respiratory fitness in older people was associated with greater activity in various areas of the brain, including a region critical for high-level cognition. And researchers at the University of Texas who found a correlation between fitness and cognitive function in middle-aged adults believe the link is at least partly down to fitness aiding better blood flow in the brain.

WORTH THE WEIGHT?

How strength training may give you a brain lift

There is plenty of literature on the effects of aerobic training on brain health. There is far less on strength training, but research suggests it, too, may benefit cognitive function. Research from the University of Montreal and the University of Poitiers, found that aerobic and strength training help the brain through two distinct and independent chemical mechanisms, both of which have a positive effect on neuron growth and survival. In the case of strength training, the improvement is due to increased levels of insulin-like growth factor 1 (IGF-1). So despite the stereotype, the weights room in the gym isn't entirely full of narcissistic meatheads, after all.

But don't start too late. Analysing data from over 1,000 men and women, Boston University School of Medicine researchers found that those who were less fit at midlife (in their 40s) had less brain tissue volume 20 years down the line. The lesson? Exercise now for better brain function later.

LONG-TERM BENEFIT

To reinforce that message, a growing body of research is showing that the long-term mental return on your investment in running may be to reduce your risk of suffering from dementia. One

RW PHARMACY
NeuroTherapyTM

DIRECTIONS
Take 1 run, 3 times per week.
WARNING Side effects may include weight loss,
health and happiness.

THE BRAIN
DRAIN

Why a tired mind saps your running

Clocking the miles may be a perfect prescription for your grey matter, but putting your mind through a tough workout beforehand won't help your run. A study published in Medicine & Science in Sports & Exercise found that when participants were asked to perform a challenging mental test designed to induce mental fatigue before a run, they selected slower, lower-intensity paces and their ratings of perceived exertion were significantly higher compared with those who watched a documentary that was not mentally taxing. If you have a hard session coming up, it might be an idea to go easy on the pre-run quantum physics.

Bottling up your emotions could also be bad news for your running performance. In another study, when volunteers were asked to hide their emotions while being shown a three-minute video designed to elicit disgust, they slowed by over three per cent in a time trial, and reported higher perceived effort. It seems the effort of suppressing natural emotional responses created mental fatigue, which affected their physical performance.

study, published in *Medicine and Science in Sports and Exercise*, found regular treadmill running early or late in life slowed cognitive decline and improved brain function in mice with a type of Alzheimer's. And research presented at the 2015 Alzheimer's Association International Conference found physical exercise may be an effective treatment for Alzheimer's and also reduces psychiatric symptoms of the disease. A study published in medical journal *The Lancet* found physical inactivity was the strongest modifiable risk factor for Alzheimer's in the UK, Europe and the US.

Much of the research has focused on the hippocampus, but running hasn't been found to only help you form memories, but also to help you better access those memories. Brain scans of early-stage Alzheimer's patients found those who exercised showed more activity in the caudate nucleus, a brain region that supports memory circuits. Running appears to improve the quality of the signals transmitted through those circuits. Yet another reason why running is just about the smartest move you can make. ■

WINING THE MIND
GAME

These research-backed mental strategies
will help you run your best

YOUR
PHOTO
HERE

Think about your running heroes – they may include Olympians as well as the pack leaders in your local running club. Most people aren't blessed with the lightning-like fast-twitch muscle fibres of Usain Bolt or the innate prowess of their club's podium climbers, but some of the traits you admire in them – their confidence, concentration and commitment - are within you. You just have to tap into your hidden potential. The mental strategies that follow are based on classic studies, along with the latest research findings in performance psychology and from conversations with sports psychologist who work with professional athletes. These expert tips will help you learn how to think, feel and act like a champion so you can develop a mindset that'll unlock your full athletic ability.

SEE SUCCESS

Imagining an optimal performance is accomplished by creating a clear mental image of what you want to achieve in a race. When visualising your ideal race, include the sights, sounds and emotions that accompany the experience. What it feels like to stand in the starting area, feeling calm and composed; and cross the finish line feeling strong and happy.

STAY POSITIVE

Identify your self-defeating thoughts and challenge them with encouraging statements. For example: 'My split time is off. I'm feeling stressed.' Stop. Breathe. Then think: 'I'm going to take a fresh, confident approach to my next mile.'

BE PRESENT

Focus all your energy on execution, not self-analysis. Don't write the review of your performance until it's over. Repeat to yourself 'Do what I can do in this moment.' That is, do your best right now and resist the urge to criticise the past or stress about the future.

PUSH ON

Mental toughness is built by doing something difficult over and over again, especially when you don't feel like doing it. The discomfort you feel when you're doing a workout is an important part of the strengthening process. Dogged determination requires keeping your feet moving forward through all those inconveniences, discomfort and insecurities to reach your goals.

DON'T PANIC

Most top athletes feel anxious before and during competition. They accept this anxiety and use it to sharpen their focus. If you're feeling nervous, remind yourself that it's necessary for optimal performance, and interpret the sensations you're feeling as signs that you're primed and ready.

PROJECT CONFIDENCE

Research shows that holding your body in confident postures for a few minutes can produce elevations in testosterone, decreases in the stress hormone cortisol and increased feelings of power. Try keeping your chin up, shoulders back and chest out.

OWN YOUR ZONE

A close relationship exists between performance quality and intensity level: your performance may be poorer when your intensity level is too low (perhaps because you feel tired) or too high (perhaps because you're overexcited). To get in the zone, you must learn to throttle up or down to find the right intensity. Athletes may be underactive in workouts ('This doesn't matter') but will hit their mental peak for races ('This means everything!'). The next time you're running, ask yourself if your intensity level is too low, too high or right where it should be. Adjust accordingly; upbeat music can help pump you up, while mellow tunes can calm you down. Dynamic stretches and strides can help prepare you for action; sitting calmly and reviewing your race strategy can help you chill out.

EVALUATE PROGRESS

Scrutinise your important workouts and races regularly. Ask yourself three questions: (1) What did I do that was good? (2) What needs to get better? (3) What changes should I make to become my best? This process will allow you to give yourself credit where credit is due and to learn from your mistakes.

REMEMBER TO FORGET

Top runners have a long-term memory for success and a short-term memory for failure. Every athlete fails, but the most successful ones do not dwell on the failures. Instead, they focus on the positive aspects of their training and racing experiences and keep confidently moving forward. ■

HEAD *GAME*

Score your mental strengths and weaknesses

Using the headings below, rate your current mental-game from 1-10, identifying strengths and weaknesses. A good initial goal score is 70. The skills are interconnected, so working on one area will improve another.

MENTAL IMAGERY	**SELF-TALK**	**FOCUS**	**MENTAL TOUGHNESS**	**ANXIETY CONTROL**
I vividly see and feel myself performing well.	I keep my thoughts simple, positive and powerful when running.	I stay on target.	I do what is hard and stay positive under adversity.	I process my nervous energy as excitement.
INTENSITY	**BODY LANGUAGE**	**PAIN MANAGEMENT**	**ANALYSIS**	**RESILIENCE**
My energy level stays just right for the situation.	I carry myself with confidence – faking it, if necessary.	I distract myself from discomfort so I can push on.	I review my progress to see if I can make improvements.	I focus on my strengths and move forward from disappointments.

CHAPTER | **6**

WOMEN'S
RUNNING

The key information women need to know before hitting the road

LADIES FIRST
Warm up your
willpower

21 TIPS FOR WOMEN *RUNNERS*

Although running is an equal opportunities sport, here are some gender-specific tips worth considering

Photography **Studio 33**

Knowledge is power, in running as in any other pursuit. The more you know about training, nutrition and health, the better you'll be at maximising your gains, whether they be fitness, weight loss, race performances or just plain fun. In this section, you'll find loads of information to help you reach your goals.

These tips cover health, psychology, pregnancy, weight loss, motherhood, training and racing, while addressing the specific needs of women.

1 ANAEROBIC RESULTS

For female runners, controlled anaerobic training – such as intervals, hills and fartlek training (see Chapter 2 for further information on how to do these) – may lead to big gains in strength and speed. Why? High-intensity anaerobic running is one of the most potent stimulators of natural human growth hormones – those that contribute to stronger muscles and enhanced performance.

2 MORNING GLORY

Running is an incredibly time-efficient way of keeping in shape, as it can be fit into even the busiest of schedules. Working out first thing in the morning means you can get the sweaty business out of the way before getting ready for work.

3 RUNNING DURING PREGNANCY

Doctors agree that moderate exercise during a normal pregnancy is completely safe for your baby. Running should cause no problems in the first trimester and it should be fine for most people in the second trimester. Few women would run in the final three months before the birth, however. The most important precaution is to avoid becoming overheated; a core body temperature above 38C could increase the risk of birth defects. So make sure you're staying cool enough, and if in doubt, take your temperature after a run. If it's over 38.3C (101F), you're probably overdoing it.

4 SHOE SELECTION

Women generally have narrower feet than men, so when buying running shoes, you're best off going for a pair designed specifically for women. That said, everyone's different, so if your feet are wide, you may feel more comfortable in shoes designed for men. The bottom line: buy the shoe that feels best on your foot. A good place to start is at a specialist running shop, where you can have your gait analysed. If there's any question – or if you suffer blisters or injuries because of ill-fitting shoes – consult a podiatrist who specialises in treating runners.

5 REDUCE CANCER RATES

An American study found women runners produce a less potent form of oestrogen than their sedentary counterparts. As a result, female runners cut by half their risks of developing breast and uterine cancer, and their risk of contracting the form of diabetes most common in women by two thirds.

6 SISTERS UNITED

Having another woman or a group of women to run with regularly will help keep you motivated and ensure your safety. It's also a lot more fun than running alone. Women runners become more than training partners – they're confidantes, counsellors and coaches, too.

7 TAKE ON THE RIGHT NUTRITION

The two minerals female runners need to pay the most attention to are calcium and iron (iron is especially important if you've got your period). Good sources of calcium are dairy products, dark leafy vegetables, broccoli, tinned sardines and salmon, while foods high in iron include liver, fortified dry cereals, beef and spinach. Vitamin C helps you absorb the iron, too.

8 TALK TO YOUR GP

Women who train intensively, have been pregnant in the past two years or consume fewer than 2,000 calories a day may require more than just the routine blood tests for iron status. This is because these test only for anaemia, which is the final stage of iron deficiency. Ask for more revealing tests, such as those for serum ferritin, transferrin saturation and total iron-building capacity.

9 PERIOD GAINS

There's no need to miss a run or a race just because you're having your period. If you're suffering from cramps, running will often alleviate the symptoms, thanks to the release of pain-relieving chemicals called endorphins. Speedwork and hill sessions can be especially effective, but use a tampon and a towel for extra protection.

10 SKIN WINS

Running helps keep your skin healthy. According to dermatologists, running stimulates circulation, transports nutrients and flushes out waste products. All of this leads to a reduction in subcutaneous fat, making skin clearer and facial features more distinct.

11 DON'T OVERDO IT

If you run so much your periods become light or non-existent, you may be endangering your bones. Amenorrhoea (lack of a monthly period) means that little or no oestrogen, essential for the replacement of bone minerals, is circulating in your body. You can stop, but not reverse, the damage by taking oestrogen and plenty of calcium. If your periods are infrequent or absent, make sure you consult a gynaecologist.

12 STRONGER BABIES

If you were a regular runner before you became pregnant, you might have a bigger baby – good news, because, up to a certain point, larger infants tend to be stronger and weather physical adversity better. Researchers in the US found women who burned up to 1,000 calories per week through exercise gave birth to babies weighing five per cent more than the offspring of inactive mums. And women who burned 2,000 per week delivered babies weighing 10 per cent more.

13 IN THE INTEREST OF SAFETY

Women who run alone should take a few sensible precautions. Leave a note at home stating when you left, where you'll be running and when you expect to return. Carry a mobile phone. Stick to well-populated areas, and don't always run the same predictable route. Avoid running at night and don't wear jewellery. Pay attention to your surroundings and recurring faces. Carry some ID, but include only your name and an emergency phone number.

14 KEEP IT REAL

Women who run purely for weight control may lose perspective on what is an appropriate body size. A recent survey of thousands of women found while 44 per cent of respondents were medically overweight, 73 per cent thought they were.

15 CHEST SUPPORT

No matter what your size, it's a good idea to wear a sports bra when you run. Controlling breast motion will make you feel more comfortable. Look for one that stretches horizontally but not vertically. Most importantly, try before you buy. A sports bra should fit snugly, yet not feel too constrictive. Run or jump on the spot to see if it gives you the support you need.

16 LATE PREGNANCY AND BIRTH

If you ran early in your pregnancy, you might want to try switching to a lower-impact exercise during the latter stages and after you've had the baby. Because of the release of the hormone relaxin during pregnancy, some ligaments and tendons might soften. This will make you more vulnerable to injury, especially around your pelvis. Walking, swimming, static cycling and aquarunning are good choices.

17 IGNORE TAUNTING

While it may not be much consolation, men are sometimes verbally harassed and/or threatened while running, just as women are. Be sensible when you run, but don't let stupid, insignificant taunting limit your freedom.

RUNNING HELPS KEEP YOUR SKIN HEALTHY AND BOOSTS YOUR CIRCULATION

HEAD FIRST
Focus on the
health benefits

18 DIARISE THOSE MONTHLY MOMENTS

'That time of the month' (or even the few days preceding it) is not the time when women run their worst. The hardest time for women to run fast is about a week before menstruation begins (a week after ovulation). That's when levels of the key hormone progesterone peak, inducing a much-higher-than-normal breathing rate during physical activity. The excess ventilation tends to make running feel more difficult.

19 MAKE SURE YOU MAKE TIME

Just because you're in a relationship or married, have a career or young children (or both) doesn't mean you don't have time to run. Running is time-efficient and the best stress-reducer on the market. You need this time. Taking it for yourself (by letting your husband or partner babysit while you run, for instance) isn't just good for you, it will benefit the whole family.

20 POST-RUN BREAST-FEEDING

Though not conclusive, some studies have suggested that babies dislike the taste of post-exercise breast milk, because it is high in lactic acid and may impart a sour flavour. It's probably a good idea to either express milk for later feeding or, if you have time, breast-feed before running.

21 PERSPIRATION INSPIRATION

It's official, women sweat less than men. And, contrary to popular belief, women dissipate heat just as well as their male counterparts. The reason is simple: women are smaller and have a higher body-surface-to-volume ratio, which means that although their evaporative cooling is less efficient, they need less of it to achieve the same result. You'll still need to take on plenty of water to prevent dehydration, though.

WOMEN'S
HEALTH

With running, women have a few extra things to consider.
Here's all you need to ensure hitting the road isn't a worry

Apart from the sort of injuries that can plague all runners – shin splints, black toenails, tendinitis – there are some health issues that can be more prevalent in women runners, and some that are exclusively female.

MENSTRUAL PROBLEMS
Although some women complain of discomfort during their periods, it is generally accepted menstruation has limited impact on exercise performance. Women have run well, set records and won titles at all phases of the menstrual cycle. Studies have shown no

onset of osteoporosis can lead to a risk of stress fractures and acute fractures, and since decreased bone density is not easily reversed, it might last for the rest of your life.

An additional concern is lack of ovulation. Because it is possible for women to menstruate even when not ovulating, the presence of a period does not guarantee a healthy menstrual cycle. A lack of ovulation can signal insufficient levels of progesterone, which can lead to overstimulation of the uterine lining, putting you at greater risk of endometrial cancer.

runners feel the pill helps performance by reducing menstrual symptoms. These runners prefer taking the pill so they can control their cycle and don't have to race when they are having their period. Although it is safe to manipulate the timing of your period, experts generally agree this practice should be reserved for major competitions and done only a few times a year.

If you run recreationally, you probably don't have to worry about any athletic impact of the pill. But if you race and don't want to sacrifice aerobic capacity, consider another type of contraception.

OSTEOPOROSIS
Exercise can help build and maintain bone density levels in women, but women who have abnormal menstrual cycles, may not gain these benefits.

> ## THERE ARE SOME HEALTH ISSUES FAR MORE PREVALENT IN FEMALE RUNNERS

change in heartrate, strength or endurance during the cycle. Exercise can improve your feelings of well-being, so some doctors recommend exercise for women who suffer some discomfort at this particular time of the month.

However, a potential problem for women who run strenuously is irregular or absent periods, which is known as athletic amenorrhoea. Training stress, performance pressure, low body fat and poor nutrition are possible contributing factors.

One of the single most serious consequences of amenorrhoea is osteoporosis. This happens when the female hormones, which serve to protect your bone's calcium, are in short supply. An early

A woman's body temperature is generally lower at the beginning of her monthly cycle and higher for the last two weeks. The increase in temperature occurs at the time of ovulation. To track this cycle, take your temperature first thing in the morning. If your conditions point towards any sort of irregularity, it's best to consult your doctor.

THE PILL
Researchers disagree about the impact of the pill on athletic performance. Though most studies have shown the pill has no effect on performance whatsoever, some research indicates it may cause a slight reduction in aerobic capacity.

On the other hand, some

Several studies have shown women who have disrupted menstrual cycles suffer more stress fractures than their counterparts with normal cycles. These women typically exhibit lower levels of bone mineral density. Although it's generally accepted that hormonal disruptions and premature loss of bone density are linked in female athletes, the cause-and-effect relationship is not clear. For example, some researchers think the kind of women drawn to intense exercise are more likely to exhibit stress in all areas of life, which could affect hormone levels even without doing a high level of exercise.

Experts agree women must act to protect themselves from early onset osteoporosis. It's particularly important, as once they are past the mid-thirties, a woman is no longer able to build bone mass, but only maintain her reserves. You should take every precaution to ensure you are not losing bone mass. That means eating a properly balanced diet – in addition to all the many important nutrients, and calcium in particular, you should make sure you are consuming the correct amount of fat and calories overall in your diet to sustain your level of exercise. Monitor your menstrual cycle, and if you notice any irregularities you should consider consulting your doctor.

INCONTINENCE

Women are more prone to stress incontinence because of their anatomy. It's estimated that one in two women experience some level of urine leakage, which can be as annoying as it is disconcerting.

Although running does not cause incontinence, the activity can induce leakage in women who are already prone to it. Many women find that strengthening the muscles in the pelvic area with Kegel exercises helps. To do these, contract your pelvic muscles as if you are attempting to stop a flow of urine. Hold for a few seconds, and then release. There are also several devices that can be bought over the counter or with a prescription that help control leakage. Talk to your GP about what might work for you.

ACNE

Women runners can be plagued by skin breakouts on their face, hairline, upper back, chest, upper arms and buttocks. Unfortunately for runners, sweat production, combined with hair follicles or friction from rubbing clothes is a formula for acne. Increased temperature and humidity exacerbate the problem, as do products such as sunscreen and make-up, which sweat off onto the skin and clog pores. To fend off acne, try the following:

RUN AND BECOME
A fitter, healthier body will be yours

■ Minimise the use of make-up and hair products before running. Wash your face before you run, and again prior to reapplying make-up after running.

■ Use a sunscreen specifically formulated for the face on your face and neck. Choose a gel or lotion for the rest of your body.

■ Always keep face wipes to hand and cleanse acne-prone areas immediately after you finish running.

■ Change out of sweaty exercise clothes straight after running, and shower as soon as possible.

■ If you are prone to acne, it's best to consult a registered dermatologist.

BORN TO RUN
There's no need to
stop running with
junior onboard

BABY
STEPS

Don't let pregnancy and parenthood stop you running. Take it all in your stride – bump, baby and beyond

Not so long ago, the notion of a woman running during pregnancy was thought of as shocking. These days the running community, at least, is supportive of its mothers-to-be, but elsewhere the idea persists that running with a bump is irresponsible. If you or your partner is expecting, you'll be anxious to know what's best for both mum and baby. The good news is that running can keep you healthy during pregnancy, happy and slim post-pregnancy, and, thanks to t he ever-increasing range of jogging buggies, you can get junior in on the act six months on. Whether you're an expectant mum or dad, or your eye's just started twinkling, you'll find everything you need to know about getting the most from your running pre- and post-bump over the following pages.

Photography **Getty, Studio 33 Media**

Q I currently run three times a week. Is it safe to continue now that I'm pregnant – and for how long?

A 'Yes, in fact medical professionals encourage women to exercise and maintain good fitness and a healthy weight,' says GP, runner and mum Dr Gemma Newman. 'Especially because obesity during pregnancy is a growing crisis. Many women will have been running for weeks before discovering they're pregnant, but don't worry that you've done yourself or the baby any harm – keeping active does you both good.' Only run if you feel up to it, though. In the first trimester you may well be too exhausted. The second trimester is usually when women 'bloom' and feel much more energetic. By the third you may be feeling more uncomfortable, so consider including some other form of training. However, there's no reason you can't jog right into the maternity ward, if that's what feels right. 'The most important thing is to listen to your body,' says Newman.

Q But are there any risks associated with running while I'm expecting?

A The main risk you face is overheating: there's a risk to your baby if your core temperature – which is already higher during pregnancy – rises further. But this is easily managed by limiting the intensity of your workouts. If you have a heart-rate monitor, stay under 75

per cent of your max. If not, 'stick to a pace at which you can easily chat, remembering the speed may change depending on conditions or how tired you are,' says running coach Karen Weir (runwithkaren.com). 'Always make sure you keep hydrated and avoid tough sessions such as tempo or threshold runs, or training in the heat. And feel free to enter events for fun, but put racing on hold.'

Again, always listen to your body. 'If you experience bleeding, dizziness, palpitations or pain – or running just doesn't feel right – stop,' says Newman. Seek and heed medical advice, 'but contrary to some people's belief, exercise isn't a major risk factor for miscarriage, nor will your baby be shaken around and damaged.'

From the second trimester, as your shape changes, bear in mind that your centre of gravity will shift and balance can go awry. 'Choose safe routes – trails, for example, are out,' says Weir. Also remember that the pregnancy hormone relaxin is coursing through your body, loosening your pelvic (and other) joints and ligaments in preparation for the birth. This increases the risk of injury. 'Be mindful of this and limit post-run

PREGNANT WOMEN WHO STAY ACTIVE HAVE SHORTER, EASIER LABOURS

stretches to a gentle 10 seconds,' says Weir.

Q Are there any expectant mothers who should avoid running?

A This is not the time to take up the sport if you've never run before, or you haven't done for some time. 'Your doctor may advise against it if you've had any bleeding or been diagnosed with an incompetent cervix,' says Newman. 'If you experience any vaginal bleeding, abdominal pain or the baby stops its normal movements, stop running and see your GP straight away.'

Q My partner's still not convinced about the benefits. What can I say?

A Numerous studies, including research published in *Clinics in Sports Medicine*, show that pregnant women who stay active have fewer delivery complications and shorter, easier labours.

In addition, research published in *Epidemiology* also found that women who exercised vigorously during pregnancy decreased their risk of premature birth, while another study in The *Journal of Obstetrics, Gynecologic and Neonatal Nursing* found it made them less likely to need a caesarean section. The study in *Clinics in Sports Medicine* also showed babies whose mothers do regular, moderate exercise have better neural development and are less likely to become overweight.

'Exercise can help get the baby in the right position, control pregnancy weight gain and boost your mood – especially important as antenatal depression is common,' says Newman. A recent US study, published in *Medicine & Science in*

RUNNING *MUMS*

Zoe Folbigg, Herts. Mum to Felix and Max

'I had to justify my decision to keep running during pregnancy. As my bump emerged and I took to the streets, I got disapproving looks, mainly from women, which upset me. At 23 weeks, I ran a 10K race and heard one horrified spectator say, "Look, how awful". It

was upsetting, but I was running with my dad who held my hand and kept me strong. As we crossed the line, I realised three generations had made it and felt a swell of pride. Ill-informed people will pass judgment, but with a thick skin you'll be fine.'

FUEL YOUR RUN
The multi-use
hydration system
for new parents...

Sports & Exercise also found aerobic exercise reduces pregnancy symptoms such as nausea, heartburn and cramps.

Q Will I need new kit to accommodate my changing body shape?

A Some maternity fitness clothing will help you look and feel the part once you've outstretched your standard Lycra. Many companies have yoga wear that will do the trick, or check out the range on fitnfabulous. co.uk. They have maternity running capri pant, T-shirts and vests. 'Your bra size will change throughout pregnancy and your breasts will probably become uncomfortable at some point,' says Weir. 'Get yours measured regularly and invest in an extra-supportive high-impact sports bra.'

Freya Active and Shock Absorber both have very good high-impact ranges, while specialist running store Sweatshop has specially trained staff to measure you for size and fit. Some women find bump bands can be helpful – try the Love Your Bump Bando (£14.99, cheekyrascals.co.uk).

Extra weight and postural changes coupled with more relaxin hormore can increase your foot size and cause overpronation. So ensure your running shoes still fit well, or consider a simple orthotic like Carnation Powerstep (from £18, amazon.co.uk).

'Even if you don't normally run with water it's wise to when you're pregnant,' suggests Weir. Use an ergonomic bottle such as the Hilly Hand Held (£3.49, sportsshoes.com). A simple heartrate monitor can also help you keep your intensity in check as you work out (try the Polar FT4, £44.70, tesco.com).

Q Running's becoming too uncomfortable now I'm bigger. How can I stay fit?

A Cross-training can help to keep you fit and strong for labour and maintain your fitness post-pregnancy. 'In late-pregnancy, cycling is out, because of the risk of falling, and the elliptical trainer can over-strain the pelvis and hips,' explains Weir.

'Walking is always good, and swimming is a fantastic full-body workout that also keeps you cool and supports your joints. A simple, light free weights routine can help boost your stamina in late pregnancy and labour.'

You should also be doing pelvic floor exercises throughout your pregnancy and look for local antenatal yoga or Pilates classes, which are a fun way to keep yourself fit and active, prep your body for labour and, of course, meet other mums-to-be.

EXERCISE CAN CONTROL PREGNANCY WEIGHT AND BOOST YOUR MOOD

RUNNING *MUMS*

Anna Scally, Surrey. Mum to Connor

'Prior to my first pregnancy, aged 37, I ran for Wales and coached at my club Ranelagh Harriers. There was no question that I'd stop running, but I did lots of research on how to modify my training, and used my knowledge as a coach and my instincts. I ran with a heart-rate monitor to keep my speed in check. At 36 weeks, I switched to swimming. I'm convinced my fitness helped with childbirth – my labour was a swift six hours and I recovered quickly. I am now pregnant again, and I will continue to run this time as well.'

BABY ON BOARD
Take motherhood
in your stride

THE MOTHERHOOD *EFFECT*

Fancy a PBPB (post-bump personal best)? It seems risible when you feel whale-like, but post-bump you could be in the shape of your life. Your organs learn to work harder when you're pregnant, while blood volume increases by up to 60 per cent to transport oxygen to the womb. And those extra cells remain for months, improving stamina. There's also evidence that mental acuity sharpens and pain threshold increases post-labour. Research in the *Scandinavian Journal of Medicine and Science in Sports* found 11 per cent of women performed better in endurance events after having a baby.

COME BACK
STRONG

Although specifically designed for a post-pregnancy return to fitness, this workout is also a great any-time, full-body routine

Carrie Tollefson, a 2004 Olympian in the 1500 metres, ran all the way through her pregnancy – right up until two days before going into labour. By the time her daughter was three months old, Tollefson was back to logging a very impressive 40 miles a week. Granted, Tollefson went into her pregnancy being incredibly fit, but she says it was the resistance traiing she did while pregnant, and after the birth, that got her back up to speed quickly and without injury. 'It's all about the gym,' says Tollefson, who at four weeks postpartum was given the green light to resume weight training up to three days a week.

'The first focus should not be returning to running,' says Tim Hilden, physical therapist at the Boulder Center for Sports Medicine. 'What's most important is rehabbing the post-delivery woman – or anyone who's gone through a setback of any sort – by strengthening the essential muscles that the body will need to recruit for running.'

Tollefson's routine, shown here, is advanced – the modified versions are a good place to start. For each exercise, do three sets of 10; progress to five sets of 10. Try to do this routine three times a week – make sure you have your doctor's permission before commencing with the routine, of course.

HAMSTRING CURLS

Strengthen glutes, hamstrings, lower back, oblique muscles, stabilising muscles of the hips and pelvis.

TOLLEFSON'S MOVE
Lie on the ground with your feet on a Swiss ball (as above). Lift your pelvis up. Then, while maintaining that position, push the ball away with your heels, then pull it back. Lower and repeat.

MODIFY IT
Place your feet on a stable object. Lift up your pelvis, lower. Progress to placing both your heels on a ball.

Photography **Sara Rusinstein**

PRESS-UPS

Strengthen upper-body and abdominal muscles.

TOLLEFSON'S MOVE
Place your hands on a medicine ball and lower down into a press-up, keeping back straight

MODIFY IT
Try a standard press-up or, easier still, push off from a wall while standing up.

PLANKS

Strengthen abdominals, obliques and glutes.

TOLLEFSON'S MOVE
Place your shins on a stability ball and your palms on the floor. Then lift one leg at a time.

MODIFY IT Rest on your forearms with your feet on the ground, and keep your back flat.

LUNGES

Strengthen hips, pelvis, quads and core muscles.

TOLLEFSON'S MOVE
Stand holding a medicine ball, with a Swiss ball behind you. Place your right leg on the ball. Then lunge down and touch medicine ball to the floor in front of you.

MODIFY IT
Do standard lunges, without balls. Progress to lunges with your back foot on a stability ball, while touching your hand to the ground in front of you.

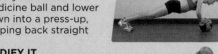

STEP-UPS

Strengthen quads, glutes, calves and core muscles.

TOLLEFSON'S MOVE
Stand with your left foot on a stool. Hold a dumbbell in your right hand. Step up and bring your right foot up in the air and lift the weight overhead.

MODIFY IT Do the same motion on a lower step and without a weight.

BICEPS AND TRICEPS

Strengthen biceps, triceps and core muscles.

TOLLEFSON'S MOVE
Do bicep curls and then overhead tricep extensions with dumbbells while you stand with both feet on a Bosu ball (a 'half' Swiss ball).

MODIFY IT While standing on one foot, do bicep curls. Then do tricep extensions.

TRAINING FOR *RACING*

Whatever distance you're training for, from a 5K to a marathon, you'll find all you need right here

FIT FOR PURPOSE
Which distance are
you built to run?

MILE 3

THE RUNNER

SPEED RACER
These athletes are built to go fast – not long. Consequently, the 5K and 10K are ideal events to target.

MIDDLE DISTANCE
These people are best at sustaining a tough pace. So they're well suited to run strong 10-milers and half marathons.

LONG-HAULER
These runners are meant to go the distance. Though lacking in speed, their true calling is the marathon.

NATURAL
SELECTION

What distance were you born to run? Here's how to figure out
what kind of runner you are – and realise your full potential

S uccess in some events comes more naturally than in others. In fact, few runners have the same potential to be outstanding at all distances. Some have the innate gift of speed, while others are natural-born long-distance runners. In the end, your physiology, temperament and priorities will determine the ideal racing distance for you.

You may be surprised to find out where your true strengths lie. 'Everyone thinks the marathon is the Holy Grail, when a lot of people should really be doing the 5K,' says Jason Karp, an exercise physiologist and running coach.

The physiology you're born with determines how well you'll perform your first time out, and how much improvement you'll be able to make in training. The good news is that with the appropriate training strategy, you can make the most of what you were born with.

So how do you determine whether you were meant to be a speed demon or an ultra-marathon runner? You could turn to pricey lab tests, but that would probably be overkill. Your running habits reveal plenty about where you'll excel.

Find which physiological factors help shape your running identity. Then examine your training, racing history and tendencies to find out which distances are perfect for you. Finally, learn how to tweak your training routine and set realistic goals to better match your newfound specialty. ➢

WHO ARE **YOU?**

Work through the following sections to find out what the type of runner you are.

A
KNOW YOUR
PHYSIOLOGY

B
IDENTIFY YOUR
TRUE CALLING

C
SET REACHABLE
GOALS

D
TRAIN LIKE
A SPECIALIST

Photography **Erik Johnson**

KNOW YOUR PHYSIOLOGY

Four qualities that influence how fast and how far you run

LACTATE THRESHOLD pace is the fastest pace that you can sustain for an extended period (roughly 30 minutes or more) before lactate – a byproduct of the fuel burned during hard exercise – starts building up in the blood. Marathon winners often have high lactate thresholds, which help them hold a strong pace for a long time. With targeted training – maintaining a certain intensity over a distance – you can raise your lactate threshold.

MUSCLES are made of slow- and fast-twitch fibres. An elite marathon runner's muscles might be 75 per cent slow-twitch; an Olympic sprinter probably has a high proportion of fast-twitch. Most runners are born with a mix of both. You can't change it, but you can train your muscles for speed or to run steady, long distances.

VO_2 MAX measures the maximum amount of oxygen that can be consumed per minute while exercising. Runners with a naturally high VO_2 max often find it easier to run faster because their hearts can deliver more oxygen to their muscles. There are many ways to boost VO_2 max – beginners can improve it by about 20 per cent. Fit runners can only fine-tune it.

RUNNING ECONOMY measures the amount of oxygen you will need to run at any pace. It reflects how efficiently you are running. Other physical factors can have an impact on your running economy – if you're overweight or have a sloppy gait, for instance, you're going to need to use more oxygen than a leaner person with a cleaner stride would. As you train by increasing your running, and improve factors like your VO_2 max, weight and biomechanics, you'll slowly develop a considerably better running economy than you had before.

IDENTIFY YOUR TRUE CALLING

What kind of running gives you the best performances

1 HOW MANY HOURS A WEEK CAN YOU DEVOTE TO TRAINING?
A 2 to 3
B 4 to 5
C 6 or more

2 HOW WOULD YOU DESCRIBE THE PERFECT TRAINING RUN FOR YOU?
A It brings a big surge of adrenaline and power channeling right through your body – like kicking into high gear.
B Running right at the edge of your abilities – not backing off, but not pushing so much that you could run out of steam.
C It's getting into a meditative rhythm, where you can zone out or get absorbed in your thoughts, a conversation or your just the scenic surroundings.

3 IF YOU COULD SKIP ANY SESSION EACH WEEK, WHAT WOULD IT BE?
A Any run that takes more than an hour. It's just too exhausting and far too boring.
B Workouts that don't feel long enough or fast enough.
C Any run where there's pressure to hold a very fast pace. It ceases to be enjoyable.

UP 4 A RUN?
What do the
numbers look
like for you?

4 WHEN ON A GROUP RUN, YOU STAND OUT FROM THE PACK BY:

A Surging to the finish, no matter how hard the group has been running.
B Managing to stick with the lead group, no matter how hard they're pushing it.
C Feeling pretty fresh at the end of a long run – no matter how far you've gone.

5 WHEN YOU GET INJURED, WHAT USUALLY CAUSES THE PROBLEM?

A Total mileage. Overdoing it always seems to trigger some ailment – like plantar fasciitis or a screaming IT band.
B A muscle pull, a tendon tweak or something that got twisted or torn while trying to keep up or dash to the finish.
C No major injuries.

6 HOW DO YOU FEEL ABOUT SPENDING MONEY ON RACING?

A With all the races I do, it's hard to justify shelling out more than £20 on just one.
B Spending £35 or so on a race is OK, as long as there aren't a lot of other costs for travel and logistics.
C No one likes to part with hard-earned cash, but for a few big events each year, it's not an issue to spend £70.

7 WHEN YOU'RE CHOOSING A RACE, WHAT MATTERS MOST?

A Convenience. Running shouldn't take time away from family, work or other important commitments.
B Getting a decent workout – and a good test – from it without having to deal with a lot of travel or other race-day logistics.
C It should feel like a big deal. Whether the race is a large, well-known event or is in a beautiful location, it should be something to circle on the calendar and look forward to, and it should feel like a reward for all the hard work I put in while training.

8 WHICH DISTANCES HAVE YOU HAD THE BEST FINISHING TIMES?

A 5K
B 10 miles or half marathon
C Marathon

ANSWER KEY
(Give yourself points as noted)

	A	B	C
1	A=2	B=4	C=6
2	A=1	B=2	C=3
3	A=1	B=2	C=3
4	A=1	B=2	C=0
5	A=1	B=2	C=0
6	A=2	B=4	C=6
7	A=2	B=4	C=6
8	A=2	B=4	C=6

How to Interpret your score
Your tally says a lot about you – your strengths, the distances you were born to run and your ideal training strategy.

10 TO 18 POINTS:
You are a Speed racer
You may not have thought about 5Ks and 10Ks since you first started running, but as you seem to be able to pick up speed with ease, that may be the place to stand out. You can put your all into it without feeling like it compromises your life to any degree.

19 TO 26 POINTS:
You are a Middle-distance specialist
It may feel like the world revolves around the marathon, but you don't have to go that far: 10-milers and half marathons could be for you. By running them, you'll find out how far and fast you can run. And as 13.1-milers become the most popular races, many have taken on the big-league feel of the famous marathons.

27 TO 34 POINTS:
You are a Long-hauler
While some people could never imagine looking forward to several hours pounding out the miles, you savour the long, slow distance running that lets you spend plenty of time outside whatever the weather. The marathon is your race. You may get left behind in a 5K by those speed racers, but that shouldn't matter. ⬎

C

SET REACHABLE GOALS

Online tools help you find the right pace and best race

BEST ONLINE TOOLS

Runners always have lots of questions. Is the marathon really for me? Is a 25-minute 5K realistic? Prediction calculators can provide some answers. These tools forecast how fast you can run one distance based on a time for another. Say you ran a 3:30 marathon, and the 5K time the calculator shows is five minutes faster than your PB. That's a clear sign that you are much more likely to perform better over a long distance race.

The predictions are based on algorithms that include factors such as race statistics and the natural tendency to run slower at longer distances. They're only accurate if you've trained for each distance.

RUNNER'S WORLD

Runnersworld.co.uk/ calculators is loaded with resources that can help you gauge how fit and fast you are – and figure out how to make your mark. It also links to SmartCoach, a tool that lets you tailor a training plan to your ability and goals.

Our race-time predictor will predict how fast you could run 11 different distances based on your performance at one race distance, and suggests training paces based on your results.

The *Runner's World* race-pace band shows the pace you need to maintain at various distances to reach your goal. Then you can create your own marathon pace band listing your splits for race day.

OTHER SITES

Mcmillanrunning.com has a tool that converts any race time to equivalent distances.

DON'T KNOW YOUR *PACE*?

Your 5K pace is a good benchmark to help you assess your fitness and set goals – whether you're running 3.1 miles or 26.2. If you haven't raced before (or for a while), this time trial, developed by exercise scientist Bill Pierce, will give you a good estimate.

1 At a track, run 3 x 1,600m (four laps) at a challenging pace, and time each segment. Jog for two minutes between intervals to recover. The goal is to run each segment at an even pace.

2 If the times of each of the three segments are similar (within 10 seconds of each other), work out your average pace per mile, then add 15 seconds. If they're markedly different try it again another day.

3 So if your segment times were 6:00, 6:04 and 6:08, your average pace is 6:04. Then add 15 seconds to get 6:19 – that time is a good estimate of your 5K pace per mile. You can repeat the test as often as you like to get an idea of where your pace is currently.

Fetcheveryone.com allows you to build a portfolio of past and future races. The site calculates your PB times over a variety of different distances.

Jeffgalloway.com has a site calculator that's especially helpful for beginners or anyone who hasn't raced before.

PACE WATCHING
It's time to find out what kind of runner you really are

D

TRAIN LIKE A SPECIALIST

Target your strengths to maximise your training gains

Once you know your strong suit, you can develop the traits that will help you excel. Of course, with focused training, you can fulfill your potential at any distance. 'Our bodies are remarkably adaptable,' says exercise scientist Bill Pierce. Work out with purpose and, he says, and 'you can reach your goals.' Here's how...

BE A SPEED RACER

(Run fast 5Ks and 10Ks)
■ **YOUR GOAL** Improve VO_2 max, fast-twitch muscles and running economy.
■ **YOUR STRATEGY** Get lots of practice running fast. Intervals, which involve working near maximum heart rate, force the heart to move as much oxygen as it can to the muscles, which boosts VO_2 max. The bursts of speed get your fast-twitch fibres firing. And as your legs and feet turn over at a quicker rate, you'll shed sloppiness and run more efficiently.
■ **KEY WORKOUT** Speedwork. Run intervals about 10 seconds faster than 5K race pace, or the quickest pace you can sustain and repeat. At a track, run 400-1,600m intervals, or on the road, run fast for up to five minutes. Between intervals, jog for two minutes. Start with three intervals.
■ **HOW TO IMPROVE** You'll need leg strength to make powerful strides and avoid injury. Twice a week, try moves such as squats and lunges to strengthen your leg muscles.

BE A MIDDLE-DISTANCE SPECIALIST

(Run 10-milers to half marathons)
■ **YOUR GOAL** Raise your lactate threshold (LT).
■ **YOUR STRATEGY** Master the art of running comfortably hard. Hold an intense pace for 20-45 minutes – this delays the time it takes for lactate to start building up in the blood and for fatigue to set in. It also builds mental stamina; you'll have more confidence in the hardest moments of the race. Don't drop speedwork and long runs – they make tempo work feel more manageable.
■ **KEY WORKOUT** Tempo run. Start with 15-20 minutes at a pace that's 15-45 seconds slower than your 5K pace. Build up to 30-45 minutes. As you become more comfortable, gradually increase the pace.
■ **HOW TO IMPROVE** Learn to breathe and relax – even during maximum effort. When you're pushing your pace, it's natural to tense up, which steals energy your heart and legs need. Running on a treadmill in front of a mirror helps you evaluate your own form and identify when you're tensing up.

BE A LONG-HAULER

(Run a strong marathon)
■ **YOUR GOAL** Improve your running economy.
■ **YOUR STRATEGY** The more you run, the more economical your form will become, and you'll feel stronger on your feet for longer. Also, your body will become more efficient at preserving energy for later in the race. Don't slack on the speedwork and tempo runs though – a strong heart and higher lactate threshold will help you stay strong for the final miles.
■ **KEY WORKOUT** The long run. Start with a one-hour run and build up to three hours. Aim to run about 30 seconds slower than your goal marathon pace. As you become more comfortable, work on picking up the pace in the middle miles. Then, shift into a higher gear in your last segment.
■ **HOW TO IMPROVE** Build a strong core and your form will be less likely to fall apart when you're fatigued. Being at your ideal weight can help, too – the lighter you are, the less oxygen you'll need. ■

GET A HEAD START
Stand side by side
with the best by
training correctly

81

TRAINING
PLANS

With the right advice, any runner can be a racer, no matter what their distance. These plans will see you over the finish line in style

---

YOUR FIRST 5K

I f you're new to running the idea of doing a race has probably crossed your mind. It's a very good idea – it will give you focus to your training and a sense of achievement once you complete it. But there's no need to overstretch yourself in the process. While a marathon might be the most high-profile race, it's a challenge you should build up to. For starters, how about a simple 5K instead? It's a perfect distance: 3.1 miles require relatively little build-up for most runners, the training doesn't take over your ▶

Illustration **Jonathan Bartlett**

life, and the race itself is over fairly quickly. And by simply logging only three or four runs per week, you could be ready to toe the line of your first 5K in just five weeks.

Top coach Chris Carmichael (trainright.com) encourages all runners to try a 5K. 'People run for a variety of reasons, but they get more out of it when they're working towards something specific,' he says. 'And a 5K race is an attainable goal for any runner.' Plus, there's the 'fun factor', says US running guru Jeff Galloway, author of *Running: Getting Started*. 'My favourite thing about 5K races is the atmosphere. Almost everyone there is in a good mood. How many other events in your life are like that?'

FIVE WEEK 5K PLAN
In the five weeks leading up to your first 5K, most coaches agree that you need to run three or four days a week. During one of those weekly runs, you should focus on increasing the amount you can run at one time until

you build to at least the race distance, or the equivalent amount of time spent running. 'I encourage runners, particularly beginners, to focus on time and effort, rather than becoming obsessed with miles and distance,' says running coach, Nick Anderson. 'Thinking in minutes is more gradual and self-paced, it will help to make sure you don't get injured by doing too much, too soon.' Completing the equivalent of the 5K distance in training gives you the strength and confidence you need to finish the race. And if you increase your long run up to six miles (or twice the amount of time it should take you to cover the 5K), you'll run with even greater strength (or speed, if you prefer).

Most of your running during the week should be at a comfortable pace. This is especially true for runners who simply want to finish the race. But because adding some faster training to your schedule is the best way to

improve your speed and endurance, even novices should really consider doing some quicker running. 'Intervals are not reserved for elites,' says Carmichael. 'Running three one-mile intervals with recovery in between will do more to increase your sustainable running pace than running three miles at once.'

First-time racers can do some faster running one or two days a week, but these sessions don't have to be regimented. Anderson recommends adapting one session per week to include about 10 minutes of speedwork, made up of two five-minute runs at a faster pace, each framed by five minutes of jogging. ➤

BEGINNER'S 5K PLAN

FIVE WEEKS TO YOUR FIRST 5K

It's training time. New runners who need to build up to the distance should follow this beginner plan

	MON	TUE	WED	THU	FRI	SAT	SUN
WEEK 1	WALK/XT 20 min or day off	RUN 10 min	WALK/XT 20 min or day off	RUN 15 min	WALK/XT 20 min or day off	REST	RUN 2 miles
2	WALK/XT 20 min or day off	RUN 15 min	WALK/XT 20 min or day off	RUN 20 min	WALK/XT 20 min or day off	REST	RUN 2.5 miles
3	WALK/XT 30 min or day off	RUN 20 min	WALK/XT 30 min or day off	RUN 25 min	WALK/XT 30 min or day off	REST	RUN 3 miles
4	WALK/XT 30 min or day off	RUN 25 min	WALK/XT 30 min or day off	RUN 30 min	WALK/XT 30 min or day off	REST	RUN 3.5 miles
5	WALK/XT 30 min or day off	RUN 30 min	WALK/XT 30 min or day off	RUN 30 min	WALK/XT 30 min or day off	REST	5K Race

Illustration **ohn Cuneo**

WACKY RACES Anyone can be a winner if you stick to a plan

INTERMEDIATE 5K PLAN

WEEK	MON	TUE	WED	THU	FRI	SAT	SUN
1	3 miles plus 5 x strides	REST	4 miles plus 5x strides	REST	4 miles plus 5 x strides	2 to 3 miles; 15-min core workout	REST
2	3 miles plus 5 x strides	REST	4 miles with 2 x 5 min at SS intensity; 15-min core workout	REST	3 miles plus 5 x strides	5 to 6 miles; 15-min core workout	REST
3	3 miles plus 6 x strides	REST	4 miles with 3 x 5 min at SS intensity; 15-min core workout	REST	3 miles plus 6 x strides	6 miles with the last 15 min at SS intensity; 15 min core workout	REST
4	3 miles plus 6 x strides	REST	4 miles with 2 x 10 min at SS intensity; 15-min core workout	REST	3 miles plus 5 x strides	6 miles with the last 15 min at SS intensity; 15-min core workout	REST
5	3 miles plus 4 x strides	REST	3 miles; 15-min core workout	REST	2 miles	2 miles plus 3 x strides	5K RACE

Once this becomes easy, try one 10-minute interval at threshold pace – this is about 85 per cent of your maximum heart rate, where you can utter a few words but not hold a conversation. Always bookend harder runs with easy warm-up and cool-down jogs.

THE BIG DAY

The greatest challenge of running your first 5K is maintaining the correct pace, says Anderson. Start out too fast and you might struggle to cross the finish line. That's why Galloway recommendsthat all first-time racers (including veteran runners) should settle at the back of the pack when at the starting line. This prevents any chance of an overzealous start and allows you to gradually build up speed during the race, ideally running the final mile the fastest. But how fast should you expect to run come race day? While Carmichael says the main goal really should be to just have fun, he tells experienced runners who are new to racing that they can expect to race about 30

seconds per mile faster than training pace. So, runners training at a nine-minute-per-mile pace should finish in around 26:25; those training at a 10-minute-mile pace should finish in 29:31; and those training at an 11-minute-mile pace should expect to finish in around 32:39.

Galloway has a very different way of predicting race times. Every two weeks, his clients run a mile around a track as fast as they possibly can. Then he uses a pace calculator, like the one that can be found online by visiting runnersworld.co.uk, to predict their times for longer distances. In general, he finds that most runners slow down about 33 seconds per mile when they go from a one-mile run to 5K race.

However, most experts will discourage first-timers from setting themselves strict time goals for race day. 'Make it a race against yourself,' says Carmichael, 'because it's your progress that will be most valuable to you.' Galloway seconds that. 'If you enjoy it, you'll do it again.' And probably faster.

BEGINNER PLAN **KEY**

WALK/XT You can walk or cross-train (swim, bike, elliptical trainer, etc) at a moderate intensity for the stated amount of time, or take the day off.
Weekday runs
All weekday runs should be at a steady pace.
Weekend long run
This is measured in miles, rather than minutes, to ensure you increase the distance you cover each week. Long-run pace should be two or three minutes per mile slower than the pace you can run one mile flat-out. Feel free to take walk breaks.

INTERMEDIATE PLAN **KEY**

Weekly mileage
Except where noted, weekly mileage should be run at a perceived effort (PE) of 6/10.
Strides
After completing the run, run hard for 20 seconds and recover with easy jogging or walking for 45 seconds; repeat as instructed.
Core workout
Do a series of basic exercises to strengthen the core muscles and improve posture.
SS intensity
Intervals at Steady State intensity should be run at a PE of seven or eight.

YOUR 10K PLAN

It's the nation's favourite distance – long enough to test your personal endurance, short enough for you to switch on the afterburners. You'll be glad to hear that 10K training forms the ideal foundation of almost all types of running performance. That's because it includes ample amounts of the three core components of distance training: strength, stamina and speed. Obviously, you can use it to train for your goal 10K, but with certain adjustments you can also use it to prepare for everything from the 5K to the marathon. Read through the runner profiles below, and decide which of our six-week plans is best for you.

WHO AM I?

BEGINNER

You're a notch above novice. You've been running at least six months, and may have done a 5K or two. You run three to five miles, three or four days a week; have done a little fast running when you felt like it; and now you want to enter – and finish – what you consider to be a real distance race.

INTERMEDIATE

You've been running a year or more, have done some 5Ks and maybe even a 10K, but you've always finished feeling as if you could or should have gone faster. You consider yourself mainly a recreational runner, but you still want to make a commitment, and see how fast you can go.

BEGINNER

If you are a beginner, your 10K goal should be less about achieving a personal best (PB) than an LDF (longest distance finished). You want to run the whole 6.2 miles, so your main aim is endurance, because it's likely to take you an hour. 'Basic aerobic strength is every runner's first need,' says running coach Bud Baldaro, so you should aim to do most of your running at a steady, moderate pace.

However, we're also going to add a dash of pseudo-speedwork into your endurance stew for flavour. This will put some added spring into your step, give you a brief taste of what it feels like to run a little faster, and hasten your progression to the Intermediate level. So, every week, in addition to your steady running, you're going to do two extra things:

AI = AEROBIC INTERVALS

In these, you push the pace until you breathe a little harder than usual. Follow with slow jogging until rested enough to resume regular speed. Always stay short of going anaerobic. ▷

BEGINNER'S 10K SCHEDULE

	MON	TUE	WED	THUR	FRI	SAT	SUN	TOTAL
1	REST	2 miles, 4 x 1 min AI, 2 miles	3 miles or REST	4 miles + 3 GP	REST	5 miles	REST	16-20 miles
2	REST	2 miles	3 miles or REST	4 miles + 3 GP	REST	5.5 miles	3.3 miles	18-21 miles
3	REST	2 miles, 4 x 90 secs, AI, 2 miles	3 miles or REST	4.5 miles + 3 GP	REST	6 miles	4 miles	18.5-22 miles
4	REST	2 miles, 6 x 90 secs, AI, 2 miles	3 miles or REST	4.5 miles + 6 GP	REST	6.5 miles	4.5 miles	20-24 miles
5	REST	2 miles, 4 x 2 min AI, 2 miles	3 miles or REST	5 miles + 6 GP	REST	7 miles	5 miles	21.5-26 miles
TAPER	REST	2 miles, 3 mins, 2 mins, 1 min AI, 2 miles	2 miles	2 miles + 2 GP	REST	REST	10K race	

INTERMEDIATE'S 10K PLAN

	MON	TUE	WED	THUR	FRI	SAT	SUN	TOTAL
1	REST	2 miles, 1-2 x 10-10, 2 miles	4 miles	400m, 800m, 1,200m, 800m, 400m PI	REST	4 miles + 4 x 100m S	6-7 miles	24 miles
2	REST	6 miles inc 6 mins TUT	4 miles	1,200m, 2 x 800m, 4 x 200m PI + 4 x 200m SI + 4 x 100m S	REST	4.5 miles + 5 x 100m S	7-8 miles	26 miles
3	REST	2 miles, 2-3 x 10-10, 2 miles	4 miles	800m, 1,200m, 800m PI + 2 x 400m SI, 4 x 100m S	REST	5 miles + 6 x 100m S	7-8 miles	27.5 miles
4	REST	6-7 miles inc 8 minutes TUT	4 miles	1,200m, 800m, 2 x 400m, 2 x 200m SI + 4 x 100m S	REST	5 miles + 6 x 100m S	8-9 miles	29 miles
5	REST	2 miles, 3-4 x 10-10, 2 mile	4 miles	800m, 4 x 400m, 4 x 200m, 800m SI, + 4 x 100m S	REST	6 miles + 6 x 100m S	8-9 miles	31 miles
TAPER	REST	800m, 2 x 200m, 400m, 2 x 200m SI + 6 x 100m S	4 miles	4 x 200m SI + 4 x 100m S	REST	3 miles easy + 3 x 100m S	10K race	

THE BIG NUMBER
Learn how to set
your goals in stone

GP = GENTLE PICK-UPS

With pick-ups, gradually increase your pace over 100 metres to 90 per cent of all-out, hold it there for 10–20m then gradually decelerate. Walk to full recovery before you do the next one. (After a few AI/GP weeks, your normal pace will feel more comfortable, and you'll get race fit more quickly.)

RACE-DAY RULES

Have a drink and an energy bar two hours before the race. Walk around for 10 minutes before the start; maybe even do a few minutes of jogging. Start off at slow, and work gradually into a comfortable and controlled pace.

INTERMEDIATE

Here's the two-pronged approach that will move you from up from recreational runner to the cusp of competitive athlete. First, you'll be adding miles to your endurance-building long run until it makes up 30 per cent of your weekly mileage. Second, you'll now be doing a substantial amount of tempo running aimed at elevating your anaerobic threshold, the speed above which blood lactate starts to accumulate in the system. You can avoid this unpleasantness with regular sustained sessions at just below 10K pace; that is, tempo-run pace.

This will significantly improve your endurance and running efficiency in just six weeks. So your training will include weekly 10-10 sessions as tempo work, along with a mix of intervals and uphill running, all of which strengthen running muscles, heart and related aerobic systems. Running fast requires effort and discomfort. But be conservative. If you can't maintain pace, or if your body starts to complain, call it a day and think about adjusting your pace next time.

Plan your training using the chart overleaf (plus you're going to need a stopwatch and a running track or known distances). Here's what the abbreviations mean.

PI = PACE INTERVALS

Run at target 10K pace to improve your efficiency and stamina, and to give you the feel of your race pace.

For 10-minute/mile pace (a 1:02:06 10K), you need to aim to run 400m in 2min 30sec (2:30); 800m in 5:00; 1,200m in 7:30.

For nine-minute/mile pace (55:53), aim to run 400m in 2:15; 800m in 4:30; 1,200m in 6:45

For eight-minute/mile pace (49:40), run 400m in 2:00; 800m in 4:00; 1,200m in 6:00.

With these pace intervals and with speed intervals (below), you should slow jog half the distance of the interval to recover.

SI = SPEED INTERVALS

Run these at 30 seconds-per-mile faster than race pace.

10-min/mile pace run 400m in 2:22; 800m in 4:44; 1,200m in 7:06.

Nine-min/mile pace 400m in 2:08; 800m in 4:16; 1,200m in 6:24.

Eight-min/mile pace 400m in 1:53 800m in 3:45; 1,200m in 5:38.

10-10

These are 10 x 10-minute tempo repetitions at 30 seconds per mile slower than 10K goal pace, with three- to five-minute slow jogs after each.

TUT = TOTAL

Uphill Time Run repetitions up the same hill, or work the uphill sections of a road or off-road course.

S = STRIDES

Over 100m, gradually accelerate to about 90 per cent of all-out, hold for five seconds, then decelerate.

Illustration **Simon Brader**

RACE-DAY RULES

'Many intermediate runners have a tendency to run too fast in the first half of the race,' says Baldaro. 'That's just about as close as you can ever get to a guaranteed way of running nothing but a mediocre time, way below your goals. Even pace is always the best way to go, which means that the first half of the race should feel really easy.' Divide the race into three two-mile sections: easy in-control pace for the first two, push yourself a bit over the middle two, then go even harder over the last two and, finally, sprint for all your worth when you see the finish line.

YOUR HALF MARATHON

The half-marathon really does have something for everyone, despite its daunting distance. Whether you're a beginner looking to stretch yourself for the first time or a marathoner who wants to stay in tune, a 13-miler could fit the bill. You might not think it, but training for a half is within reach for all runners. Our three-day-a-week beginner's and improver's schedules, devised by coach Nick Anderson (runningwithus.com), will show you how.

The beginner runner's training schedule lets you run by measuring time spent and your own effort levels, rather than counting out the miles. It's designed for those who have never competed in a half-marathon before and allows them to build from 30-minute run/walk sessions to competing on race day over a 12 week plan.

The improver's programme is, of course, somewhat more advanced. It's designed specifically for runners who have already competed in at least a few half-marathons, but are looking to make a marked improvement on their personal best time. It's also a good training plan for anyone eager to maintain marathon fitness when they have six months or more between races.

'Improvers should certainly be looking at sub two hours, specifically 1:50, but I've actually coached runners who have been able to run under 1:30 for a half-marathon just by training with this three-day-weekly schedule,' says Anderson. You should guage your effort using your rate of perceived exertion, as described in the box below, or keep a track of your heart rate using a monitor.

KEY TO PERCEIVED EFFORT (PE)

5 (out of 10) or 50% maximum heart rate (max HR)
This is a brisk walk, never a jog.

6 (out of 10) or 60% max HR
Recovery running. This is a very easy running pace that allows you to maintain a conversation with a running partner without gasping for breath.

7 (out of 10) or 70% max HR
Steady running. A little harder than recovery pace, but you should still be able to hold a conversation.

8 (out of 10) or 80% max HR
Threshold running and target half-marathon pace. You should only be able to say a few words.

8.5+ (out of 10) or 85% max HR
This is just below your maximum effort and you won't be able to speak. Use for intervals and speed work.

BEGINNER'S HALF-MARATHON SCHEDULE

WEEK	MON	TUES	WED	THURS	FRI	SAT OR SUN
1	REST	30 mins: 5-min walk/5-min run, repeat 3 times. PE: 5/7	REST	30 mins: 1-min walk/ 1-min easy jog/1-min run, repeat continuously. PE: 5/6/7	REST	30 mins: 5-min walk/5-min run, repeat 3 times. PE: 5/7
2	REST	30 mins: 4-min walk/6-min run, repeat 3 times. PE: 5/7	REST	30 mins: 2-min walk/2-min easy jog/2-min run, repeat continuously. PE: 5/6/7	REST	30 mins: 4-min walk/6-min run, repeat 3 times. PE: 5/7
3	REST	30 mins: 2-min walk/8-min run, repeat 3 times. PE: 5/7	REST	30 mins: 2-min walk/2-min easy jog/2-min run, repeat continuously. PE: 5/6/7	REST	30 mins of 2-min walk/8-min run, repeat 3 times. PE: 5/7
4	REST	30 mins: 2 x 10 mins of continuous easy running. Have a 5-min walk between blocks. PE: 5/7	REST	45 mins: 3-min walk/3-min jog/3-min threshold run, repeat continuously. PE: 5/6-7/8	REST	50 mins: 2-min walk/8-min run, repeat 4 times. Have a 5-min brisk walk warm-up & cool-down. PE: 5/7
5	REST	20 mins continuous running with 5-min walk warm-up and cool-down. PE: 5/7	REST	Repeat above session	REST	60 mins: 3-min walk/12-min run, repeat 4 times. PE: 5/7
6	REST	25 mins continuous running with 5-min walk warm-up and cool-down. PE: 5/7	REST	5-min walk/5-min easy run/5-min threshold run, repeat 3 times. PE: 5/6-7/8	REST	Repeat above session
7	REST	30 mins easy-pace run with 5-min walk warm-up and cool-down. PE: 5/7	REST	45 mins: 5 x 5-min threshold / 2-min walk & 5-min warm-up and cool-down. PE: 5/8	REST	75 mins: 3-min walk/12-min run, repeat 5 times. PE: 5/7
8	REST	40 mins easy pace with warm-up and cool-down walks. PE: 5/7	REST	5-min threshold/5-min easy run, x 2 with warm-up walk/jog and cool-down. PE: 5/8	REST	Repeat above session
9	REST	45 mins easy pace with warm-up and cool-down walks. PE: 5/7	REST	30 mins: 5-min easy/5-min threshold. Add a 5-min warm-up and cool-down jog. PE: 5/6-7/8	REST	90 mins: 3-min walk/12-min run, repeat 6 times. PE: 5/7
10	REST	45 mins easy. PE: 6-7	REST	40 mins: 5-min easy/5-min threshold. Add a 5-min warm-up and cool-down jog. PE: 5/6-7/8	REST	100 mins: 18-min easy run/ 2-min walk, repeat 5 times. PE: 5/6-7
11	REST	30 mins: 10 very easy jog/10 steady/10 threshold PE: 6/7/8	REST	40 mins easy pace: 2 x 10 mins threshold. Have 5-min jog between efforts. PE: 6/8	REST	60 mins: 25 mins easy pace/ 5 min walk, repeat 2 times PE: 5/6-7
12	REST	30 mins: 5-min easy/5-min threshold, repeat 3 times PE: 6/8	REST	20 mins easy relaxed run. PE: 6-7	REST	Race Day 15-20 mins easy pace/walk 5 mins. Drink while walking. PE: 5/6-8

IMPROVER'S HALF-MARATHON SCHEDULE

	MON	TUES	WED	THURS	FRI	SAT OR SUN
WEEK **1**	REST	10 mins easy/8 mins @ threshold pace, repeat 2 times. PE: 6-7/8-8.5	REST	10 mins easy, 2 x 5 mins of continuous hills (approx 45 secs up/45 secs down), 10 mins easy. PE: 6-7/8-8.5	REST	60 mins easy PE: 6-7
2	REST	10 mins easy, 10 mins @ threshold pace, repeat 2 times. PE: 6-7/8-8.5	REST	10 mins easy, 2 x 7 mins of continuous hills, 10 easy. PE: 6-7/8-8.5	REST	70 mins easy. PE: 6-7
3	REST	7 mins easy, 7 mins @ threshold, repeat 3 times. PE: 6-7/8-8.5	REST	10 mins easy, 3 x 5 mins of continuous hills, 10 easy. PE: 6-7/8-8.5	REST	75 mins easy PE: 6-7
4	REST	36 mins: 6 x 3 mins, with 3 mins easy in between Reps 1, 3 & 5 @ PE: 6-7; reps 2, 4 & 6 @ PE: 8-8.5	REST	40-min hilly run. Easy but faster up hills PE: 6 if easy, PE: 7-8 if hilly run	REST	60 mins easy or 10K race. PE: 6-7 or 8-9
5	REST	45 mins relaxed. PE: 6-7	REST	10 mins easy, 2 x 10 mins of continuous hills (approx 45 secs up/45 secs down), 10 easy. PE: 6-7/8-8.5	REST	80 mins easy PE: 6-7
6	REST	5 mins easy, 2 x 12 mins @ threshold/HM race pace with 4 mins easy recovery, 5 mins easy. PE: 6-7/8-8.5	REST	10 mins easy, 3 x 7 mins of continuous hills, 10 mins easy. PE: 6-7/8-8.5	REST	80 mins with last 20 mins @ HM race pace. PE: 6-7/8
7	REST	45 mins: 15 easy, 15 steady, 15 threshold. PE: 6/7/8	REST	40 mins hilly run. Attack the hills, relax rest of run. PE: 6-7/8-8.5	REST	60 mins easy. PE: 6-7
8	REST	5 mins easy, 3 x 10 mins @ threshold/HM pace, 5 min easy. PE: 6-7/8-8.5	REST	10 mins easy, 3 x 8 mins of continuous hills, 10 mins easy. PE: 6-7/8-8.5	REST	90 mins easy with 20 mins @ HM race pace. PE: 6-7/8
9	REST	10 mins easy, 25 mins @ HM/threshold pace, 10 mins easy. PE: 6-7/8-8.5	REST	10 mins easy, 2 x 6, 4, 2 mins @ HM, 10K, 5K pace with 2-min easy between sets, 10 easy. PE: 6-7/8-9	REST	100–110 mins easy. PE: 6-7
10	REST	10 min easy, 5 x 2 min hard/2 min easy, 10 min easy. PE: 6-7/8-9	REST	45 mins hilly run or 40 mins easy if racing Sunday. PE: 6/7 or 8	REST	75 min easy OR 10K race. PE: 6-7 or 9
11	REST	48 mins: 3-min threshold/3-min easy, repeat 8 times PE: 6-7/8-8.5	REST	15 mins easy, 5 x 3 mins @ 10K pace with 2-min easy recovery between each rep, 15 mins easy. PE: 6-7/9	REST	60 mins easy. PE: 6-7
12	REST	30 mins: 5 mins easy/5 mins @ threshold, repeat 3 times. PE: 6/7	REST	20 mins easy. PE: 6	REST	Half-Marathon Race. PE: 8

THE GOLDEN RULES OF 26.2

The 12 commandments that every marathon runner should follow

When I did my first marathon in 1976, the event was for experienced runners aiming to break three hours,' says running coach Steve Smythe. 'Thirty-six years on, well over a million people of all speeds, shapes and sizes have run one. It's a very honest sport: put the work in and you usually get the rewards. Here are the 12 golden rules I've learnt in three-and-a-half decades of marathon running.'

1 BUILD UP TO IT

If you want to run a successful marathon, don't rush into it. Start with shorter events, gain experience and build endurance, then tackle a marathon when you get fitter and stronger. Paula Radcliffe and Haile Gebrselassie had been running for well over 10 years before attempting their first marathon. I regret running my first aged just 18. I trained well for a few months but wasn't ready, started too fast and much of the last 10K was walked. I ran 2:54:42, but was capable of quicker.

2 LONG RUNS ARE KEY

Whether you want to run sub-3:00 or sub-5:00 for the marathon, the key session is the weekly long run. The more you do, the better your endurance. Other runs – speedwork, midweek distance runs and marathon-pace runs – have their place but they're not as crucial. The key to a good marathon is how well you hold your pace in the last 10K and that comes from doing plenty of long runs. I do about six long runs of around 20 miles across the 15 weeks before the marathon. That gives me the confidence I need to know I can hold a pace over the second half, when the going starts getting tough.

3 BE CONSISTENT, BE SENSIBLE

Consistent training (for example, 15 weeks at 40 or 50 miles a week) is better than five weeks at 100, then five weeks off through injury. However, it is best to miss a few days if you aren't feeling well or have an injury, rather than run through it and make yourself feel worse. Many runners lose sight of the fact rest is a vital component in any schedule. Yes, there has to be some training in which you get used to running while tired, but do this too often and you could break down.

4 RACE OTHER DISTANCES

Races are more fun than training and you can practise pacing, hydration and running in crowds. I'd suggest running a half marathon, 10K or 10-miler once a month to monitor your progress. The merits of a 20-mile race are more debatable. It's probably fine for a marathon-pace run, scheduled four to six weeks before the marathon, but a flat-out 20-mile race will probably take more away from your marathon than it will enhance it. In my 30s, I ran some very good 20-mile races in March but never got near that pace when I did the marathon a month later.

5 DON'T SKIMP ON SPEED

On the face of it, 26.2 miles doesn't seem to require a great deal of speed – endurance is the key. However, there is a link between your 10K ability and what marathon time you can run. A sub-3:00 marathoner, for example, needs to be able to be able to run around 40 minutes for 10K. A sub-3:00 marathon translates as 43:40 for each 10K segment, and if you are going to put four of those back to back then you're not going to be comfortable if 41 minutes is near your limit.

6 GET TREATMENT

Sometimes a small niggle can become a serious injury. Getting it sorted quickly before an injury develops could save a lot of frustration. A good sports therapist will be able to spot a problem before it prevents you from training, so booking in for regular massages is worthwhile. It's only regular visits to the osteopath, physio and sports therapist, together with more stretching, core and weights work, that has kept me training and able to race regularly.

7 TRAIN SMARTER AS YOU AGE

As you get older, speed decreases, stride length

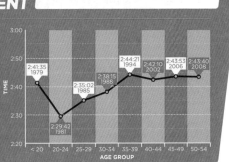

initially to err on the side of caution. Before you run a marathon, you should know fairly well what pace you will attempt based on your training, past races, recent injuries, weather conditions, the course profile and even your age.

11 PACE SENSIBLY
Many marathon runners do everything perfectly in training and then blow it during the race by suddenly deciding they feel great and attempt a pace they have never raced at before. Invariably this leads to a good first half followed by a painful second half and a time much slower than you are capable of. I used to blast out in marathons and hang on, but I paced my sub-2:30 PB more sensibly and in later years my key has been to conserve as much energy as possible over the first 20 miles, so I'm at my freshest for the crucial last 10K.

12 RECOVER & REVIEW
The most important thing after a marathon is to rest and recover. However the race has gone, take some positives from it and congratulate yourself on the achievement. At some point, analyse what went right and wrong in training and the race so you can make adjustments for next time. And don't return to hard racing too soon. The body may seem to have recovered but a speed session or race can show otherwise – as I have found to my cost in recent years. Recharge both your batteries and motivation for your next challenge.

DISTANCE LEARNING
Try a variety of shorter races to practise your pacing

shortens, recovery takes longer and injuries increase. For my first 30 years of marathoning, I stayed fairly healthy despite sometimes doing crazy things like running a pair of sub-3:00 marathons in a week, twice in the same year. But if I'd carried on doing that, I have no doubt in my mind that I wouldn't be running respectable times in my 50s. I now focus on one marathon a year, give my body a rest from long runs during the summer and work more on speed. I don't train as hard as I used to, but I train smarter: resting more, staying offroad where I can and doing speedwork on grass. Consequently I have been able to stay at pretty much the same level from my 30s to my early 50s.

8 FUEL YOUR EFFORTS
Good nutrition and hydration can make a huge difference, both in training and in racing. The biggest change in my marathons over the last 10 years or so is my use of energy gels. I regularly used to run out of energy in the last six miles but since using gels, I have been far stronger over the closing miles. I usually find four is sufficient for my needs in the marathon.

9 HAVE A TARGET
It is important to have a target to keep you motivated. Early on, it helped me to tell others what time I was aiming for to increase my drive. But in later years the motivation has been to do well in my age group, or to help others. Two years ago I ran with someone doing their first marathon, while last year, on limited training, my goal was to extend my sub-3:00 streak to over 35 years.

10 BE REALISTIC
It helps to know what time you are capable of in a marathon and then adjust your pace to that time. Until you have the experience of knowing how your body will react past 20 miles in a race situation it is best

Photography Getty

MISTER CONSISTENT

Steve Smythe says his marathon PB of 2:29:42 is 'nothing special' (though we would disagree). But his consistency, which spans five decades of sub-3:00 marathon running, from his teens to his 50s, is truly remarkable. Here are his best times in five-year age groups.

AGE GROUP	TIME
< 20	2:41:35 1979
20-24	2:29:42 1981
25-29	2:35:02 1985
30-34	2:38:15 1988
35-39	2:44:21 1994
40-44	2:42:10 2002
45-49	2:43:53 2006
50-54	2:43:40 2008

PLAN AHEAD
Reach race day
ready for the
challenge

YOUR FULL MARATHON

You can conquer your first 26.2 mile race with this thorough training plan which uses a combination of gradual build-up, speedwork and goal-paced runs to get you fit and raring to go. Follow each stage carefully and judge how well you are doing by the times and distances provided. Keep your perceived effort in check, as going too hard or too easy at the wrong point in the plan could hinder your training. Ready for a challenge? They don't come much bigger than a full-length marathon.

KEY TO BEGINNER'S MARATHON *SCHEDULE*

EASY Run or cross-train at a conversational pace (40-60 seconds slower per mile than your usual marathon pace).

LSD Long, slow distance run that builds endurance. Run at a conversational pace. LSDs are rehearsals for racing – use them to determine your gear choices and strategies for the big day.

MP Marathon goal pace. After warming up properly for at least one mile, practise the speed you hope to hit at the race. Cool down by slowing your pace to easy running.

REST Ideally, do no exercise. Non-impact cross-training such as stretching, yoga, or swimming can be beneficial instead.

YASSO 800s Warm up with one to two miles Easy running, then run 800 metres in the time that's equal to your marathon goal time. So for example, if you're targeting a 4:30 marathon, run each 800 in four minutes and 30 seconds. Jog 400 metres between repeats. Cool down with Easy running.

Illustration **Marcos Chin**

BEGINNER'S MARATHON SCHEDULE

WEEK	MON	TUES	WED	THURS	FRI	SAT	SUN	TOTAL
1	REST	4 miles EASY	4 miles EASY	4 miles EASY	REST	3 miles EASY	10 miles LSD	25
2	REST	4 miles EASY	5 miles EASY	4 miles EASY	REST	3 miles EASY	12 miles LSD	28
3	REST	3 miles EASY	5 miles EASY	3 miles EASY	REST	5 miles EASY	14 miles LSD	30
4	REST	3 miles EASY	4 miles EASY w/2 miles @ MP	4 miles EASY	REST	3 miles EASY	10 miles LSD	24
5	REST	3 miles EASY	6 miles EASY w/2 miles @ MP	4 miles EASY	REST	3 miles EASY	16 miles LSD	32
6	REST	5 miles EASY	4 miles EASY w/4 x 800	Yasso 800s 5 miles	REST	3 miles EASY	18 miles LSD	35
7	REST	5 miles EASY	7 miles EASY w/3 miles @ MP	5 miles EASY	REST	3 miles EASY	20 miles LSD	40
8	REST	5 miles EASY	8 miles EASY	3 miles EASY	REST	3 miles EASY	13 miles LSD or half marathon	32
9	REST	7 miles EASY	8 miles EASY w/5 miles @ MP	7 miles EASY	REST	5 miles EASY	16 miles LSD	43
10	REST	5 miles EASY	3 miles EASY w/6 x 800	Yasso 800s 5 miles	REST	5 miles EASY	18 miles LSD	38
11	REST	4 miles EASY	7 miles EASY w/5 miles @ MP	5 miles EASY	REST	4 miles EASY	20 miles LSD	40
12	REST	7 miles EASY	7 miles EASY w/4 miles @ MP	6 miles EASY	REST	4 miles EASY	18 miles LSD	42
13	REST	7 miles EASY	3 miles EASY	7 miles EASY	REST	3 miles EASY	20 miles LSD	40
14	REST	5 miles EASY	6 miles EASY w/8 x 800	Yasso 800s 8 miles	REST	3 miles EASY	13 miles LSD	35
15	REST	5 miles EASY	7 miles EASY	5 miles EASY	REST	5 miles EASY	10 miles LSD	32
16	REST	6 miles EASY	REST	5 miles EASY	REST	1-3 miles EASY	EASY RACE DAY	40.2

THE FAST LANE
Follow the road to
successful running

The *Runner's World* race-tested marathon-training programme will get you across the finish line in 3:59:59 – or better! – with early hill work, later tempo sessions and strategic goal-pace runs

KEY TO INTERMEDIATE MARATHON *SCHEDULE*

HILLS Run the mileage for the day on the hilliest course you can find. Focus on sustaining an even effort as you climb and descend. If you live in a flat area then run intervals (known as speedwork) instead.

TIME TRIAL Go to a local 400m track or any one-mile stretch of road. After 10 minutes of walking and jogging, run one mile, or four laps of the track. Over the course of training, your fitness gains will be reflected in your time trials.

MP Marathon goal pace. Practise the

speed you're hoping to hit in the race. Warm up and cool down.

TEMPO RUN Run Easy for one to two miles as a warm-up. Then dial into the pace that's given. Run Easy for two miles to cool down.

YASSO 800s Warm up with two miles of Easy running, then run 800 metres at the given pace that's "equal" to your marathon time.

LONG RUNS Later in the programme, pick up the pace in the last two to three miles for a fast finish.

Illustration **Simon Brader**

INTERMEDIATE MARATHON SCHEDULE

WEEK	MON	TUES	WED	THURS	FRI	SAT	SUN	TOTAL
1	REST	4 miles EASY (10.04/mile)	Hills: 4 miles	REST	4 miles EASY (10.04/mile)	4 miles EASY (10.04/mile)	9 miles EASY (10.04/mile)	25
2	REST	4 miles EASY (10.04/mile)	Hills: 5 miles	REST	5 miles EASY (10.04/mile)	5 miles EASY (10.04/mile)	9 miles EASY (10.04/mile)	28
3	REST	3 miles EASY (10.04/mile)	Hills: 5 miles	REST	5 miles EASY (10.04/mile)	5 miles EASY (10.04/mile)	12 miles EASY (10.04/mile)	30
4	REST	4 miles EASY (10.04/mile)	Hills: 5 miles	TRIAL TIME	4 miles EASY (10.04/mile)	4 miles EASY (10.04/mile)	11 miles EASY (10.04/mile)	28
5	REST	4 miles EASY (9:58/mile) with 4 strides	Hills: 7 miles	REST	4 miles with 2 miles @ MP (9:09/mile)	4 miles EASY (9:58/mile)	13 miles EASY (9:58/mile)	32
6	REST	5 miles EASY (9:58/mile) with 5 strides	Hills: 6 miles	REST	4 miles with 2 miles @ MP (9:09/mile)	6 miles EASY (9:58/mile)	15 miles EASY (9:58/mile)	36
7	REST	6 miles EASY (9:58/mile) with 6 strides	Hills: 7 miles	REST	5 miles with 3 miles @ MP (9:09/mile)	5 miles EASY (9:58/mile)	16 miles EASY (9:58/mile)	39
8	REST	5 miles EASY (9:58/mile) with 5 strides	Hills: 8 miles	REST	Time trial	4 miles EASY (9:58/mile)	14 miles of half marathon	32
9	REST	3 miles EASY (9:52/mile) with 3 strides	Tempo: 8 miles with 3 miles @ 8:30/miles	REST	9 miles with 7 miles @ MP (9:09/mile)	3 miles EASY (9:52/mile)	18 miles EASY (9:52 pace) fast finish	41
10	REST	4 miles EASY (9:52/mile) with 4 strides	Yaso 8000s: 9 miles with 6x 800s at 3:57	REST	10 miles with 8 miles @ MP (9:09/mile)	REST	20 miles EASY (9:52 pace) fast finish	43
11	REST	4 miles EASY (9:52/mile) with 4 strides	7 miles EASY (9:52/mile)	REST	10 miles with 8 miles @ MP (9:09/mile)	4 miles EASY (9:52/mile)	20 miles EASY (9:52 pace) fast finish	45
12	REST	7 miles EASY (9:52/mile)	Tempo: 9 miles with 5 miles @ 8:30/miles	6 miles EASY (9:52/mile)	TIME TRIAL	8 miles EASY (9:52/mile)	15 miles EASY (9:52/mile)	45
13	REST	5 miles EASY (9:46/mile) with 6 strides	Yaso 8000s: 10 miles with 8x 800s at 3:57	REST	6 miles EASY (9:46/mile)	5 miles EASY (9:46/mile)	22 miles EASY (9:46/mile)	48
14	REST	8 miles EASY (9:46/mile) with 8 strides	Tempo: 8 miles with 4 miles @ 8:20/miles	REST	7 miles EASY (9:46/mile)	7 miles EASY (9:46/mile)	15 miles of half marathon	45
15	REST	5 miles EASY (9:46/mile) with 5 strides	Tempo: 5 miles with 3 miles @ 8:20/miles	REST	5 miles EASY (9:46/mile)	5 miles EASY (9:46/mile)	12 miles EASY (9:46/mile)	32
16	REST	5 miles EASY (9:46/mile) with 5 strides	REST	5 miles EASY (10:04/mile)	REST	3 miles EASY (10:04/mile)	RACE DAY (9:09/mile)	39.2

WHY LESS IS *MORE*

To race your best, you need to get enough rest beforehand. But can you have too much of a good thing?

Tapering – scaling back your miles to allow your muscles to repair and your body to rest – is the critical last phase of training before a race. It's no less important to achieving the time you want than, say, long runs. But consider this: trimming your mileage right back abruptly might not be the best move. In fact, maintaining a higher volume during the taper period can give you a better chance of hitting peak performance on the big day.

'The problem with a big cut in mileage is that your body gets used to being on holiday,' says exercise physiologist Greg McMillan. Running coach Jack Daniels puts it more bluntly:

'You can taper too much.'

Just as you can add miles too quickly (and get injured), cutting them drastically can lead to a sluggish or sickly feeling. It's not uncommon even for elite athletes to come down with a stinking cold the week before a big race. One possible reason is that a major mileage cut could send a signal to the immune system that it's OK to ease up. By maintaining volume, however, your immune response will remains consistent.

McMillan not only maintains more of his runners' miles in the days leading up to a race, he also shortens the taper (two weeks for a marathon, seven to 10 days for a half). He says today's recreational runners simply don't need as much rest as those of 30 years ago. That's because they generally log 30-40 miles per week instead of 70, making a heavy taper unnecessary. In addition, he says, 'We understand the recovery cycle better.' Today's training programmes have rest and

recovery built into them, so overtraining is less likely. The key to a successful taper is some cutback in total mileage combined with a little quality work. McMillan suggests reducing your volume by 10-40 per cent, depending on race distance and fatigue level. A 5K, of course, requires less of a reduction and a shorter taper than a marathon. Similarly, low-mileage runners need less taper time than long-haulers.

It's best to reduce volume by eliminating miles from each of your weekly runs. Do a shorter long run, fewer miles on easy days and less higher-intensity work (instead of eight 800s, run four; instead of four tempo miles, do two). Just don't cut

out quality altogether – multiple studies show some fast-paced running is critical to keeping your lungs and legs sharp.

Keep in mind that every athlete is 'an experiment of one', says Daniels. Percentages and time lines are guides – use them as a place to start, and adjust accordingly. Test your fatigue level a week or two before your taper by doing a two- to six-mile run at race pace. If you feel sluggish you might need to extend your taper by a few days or reduce your mileage by another five to 10 per cent. 'A taper is part physiological, part psychological,' says Daniels. 'If it doesn't settle in your mind, it interferes with the benefits come race day.'

TAPER YOUR **DIET**

Tweaking your food intake is key to your pre-race prep. Use this guide to help you fuel up right

7 DAYS BEFORE	4 DAYS BEFORE	2 DAYS BEFORE	NIGHT BEFORE	RACE DAY
For marathon runners only: reduce your intake by 100 calories for every mile you knock off your training.	For all distances: start carb-loading now. Aim for 500g per day. Wholegrain pasta or bread is ideal.	Start fluid-loading. Sports drinks are good, but water will do.	Eat a high-carb meal containing 800-1,000 calories. Stick to what you know – your stomach doesn't want any surprises on race day.	Eat 800 calories of low-fat carbs up to two hours before.

NECESSARY **CUTBACKS**

Tapering correctly is critical to keeping you fired up and injury-free on race day. This easy-to-follow guide shows you how

5K OR 10K	**7 DAYS BEFORE** Reduce weekly mileage by 10-20 per cent. Do 3-5 x 3 min at your goal 5K or 10K pace, with 1 min rest in between	**4** Rest or run according to your schedule		**2 OR 1** Rest or run according to your schedule	
½ MARATHON	**10 DAYS BEFORE** Reduce your weekly mileage by 10-20 per cent	**7** 10 miles, with the last 2-3 miles at half-marathon pace	**4** 5 x 3 min at your target half-marathon pace, with 1min rest in between	**2 OR 1** Rest or run according to your schedule	
MARATHON	**14 DAYS BEFORE** Reduce your weekly mileage by 10-20 per cent	**12** 10 x 400m at your 5K pace, with 1 min rests	**10** 3 x 2K at 10K pace, 2-3 min rests	**7** Reduce mileage by another 10-20 per cent; 12-mile run with last 6 at race pace	**4** 4 x 3 min at 10K pace, 1 min rests in between	**2 OR 1** Rest or run according to your schedule

INDEX